MOTHER Necessity

Gluten Free/Casein Free Recipes

Finally, your favorite foods Allergen Free.

By Cristin L. Fergus

MOTHER

Necessity™

Published by
Mother Necessity, Inc.
PO Box 600784
Jacksonville, FL 32260

www.MotherNecessity.com

Mother Necessity Gluten Free/Casein Free Recipes
Newly Revised and Expanded
SECOND EDITION

Copyright @ 2008 by Cristin L. Fergus

PLEASE NOTE: The author of this work is not a physician. This work is based on research by the author, and the ideas, procedures, and suggestions in this book are not intended to substitute for the individualized medical evaluation and advice of a qualified, licensed health professional. The author does not recommend eliminating medications or implementing dietary changes without consulting with a personal physician. Any person suffering from adverse health conditions and family history require an individualized health plan.

The author disclaims any liability arising directly or indirectly from the use of this book, including dietary changes, suggestions interventions, products, or recipes. The statements made by the author represent the author's personal views and opinions, and do not constitute an endorsement of any dietary changes, products, or treatment.

ISBN 978-0-9796579-3-1
$19.95 Softcover

1. Health. 2. Nutrition. 3. GF/CF recipes. 4. Food Allergies 5. Special Diets

Cover Design: Maryellen Margossian
Interior Design: Maryellen Margossian
Print Production: Century Type, Inc.

Acknowledgments

To all of the individuals looking to enhance their health and well being I applaud you. It is not always an easy task. I encourage everyone to continue to pursue healthy living options, as they have personally offered me and my family clarity and better quality of life.

As we begin to take responsibility for our own health, it is amazing the transformations that begin to take place. I hope the information in this book can support *your* transformation and promote good health and well being.

To my loving husband Joe and my beautiful son Dylan I thank you for all of your support and love. You are the source of my strength and inspiration.

Joe, I thank you for your patience and selflessness. Without you, none of this would have been possible. You have always believed in me and have encouraged me to make a difference in this world.

Dylan, you never cease to amaze me. You are the most incredible human being that I have ever met. You have given me faith in the human body and the human spirit. You have taught me that the body can do amazing things, and it is much simpler than I could have ever imagined. You have broadened my awareness and have renewed my life. You are a true blessing and Mommy and Daddy are so proud of you!

To all of our friends and family we thank you for your support and encouragement. To my heavenly family, I thank you for your guidance and wisdom. Your light and love is the inspiration behind everything that I do.

Contents

Acknowledgments 3

Mother Necessity Recipe
   Information 6

Raw Foods 6

Dylan/Multiple
   Chemical Sensitivity (MCS) 7

Gluten 7-8

Dairy/Casein 9

Soy 9-10

Gluten Free/Casein Free Diets 10-11

Important GF/CF Facts 11

Why Whole Foods 11-12

Why Organic 12

Free Range Meats 12-13

Chemicals 13

Food Additives 13-14

Food Allergies and Intolerances 14-15

Leaky Gut 15

Rotating Foods 16

Blood Sugar 16

Healthy Fats 16-17

Nutrition 17-18

Cooking out of Necessity 18

Whole Food Preparation 18-19

Soaking Directions 19

Mother Necessity Nuritional
   Contributions 20-24

Getting Started 24

What you will need 24-25

Guidelines for nuts and seeds 25

Important Tips 25-26

Recipes

Cookie Recipes **27-35**

Pumpkin Cookies 28

Almond Cookies 29

Apple Cinnamon Cookies 30

Peppermint Cookies 31

"Green" Carob Cookies 32

"Mock" Oatmeal Cookies 33

Chocolate Cookies 34

"Mock" Chocolate Chip Cookies 35

Breakfast Ideas **36-41**

Almond Cereal 37

Apple Cinnamon Cereal 38

"Mock" Oatmeal Cereal 39

Chocolate Cereal 40

Pumpkin Spice Cereal 41

Milk Alternatives **42-43**

Almond Milk 43

Sunflower Milk 43

Probiotic Milk 43

Muffins, Cupcakes and
Brownies **44-50**

Golden Muffins or Cupcakes 45

Apple Cinnamon Muffins 46

Pumpkin Muffins 47

"Green" Carob Muffins 48

"Mock" Oatmeal Muffins 49

Brownies 50

Raw Frostings............................**51-53**

Chocolate Frosting 52

Green Mint Frosting.............................52

"Mock" Chocolate Frosting.................53

Vanilla Frosting 53

Flatbreads **54-50**

Millet Flat Bread 55

Quinoa Flat Bread................................56

Brown Rice Flat Bread 57

Crackers **58-61**

Millet Flat Bread Crackers....................58

Quinoa Flat Bread Crackers 59

Brown Rice Flat Bread Crackers...........60

Almond Crackers 61

Cracker Topping Ideas...............**62-62**

Basic Avocado Dip 62

Basic Almond and Spinach Dip 62

Basic Almond Butter.............................62

Basic Pumpkin Seed Butter 62

"Mock" Peanut butter made
with Sunflower Seeds 62

**French toast, Waffles and
Pancakes** **63-65**

Millet Flat French Toast 63

Quinoa Pancakes with
Glycerin Syrup 64

Brown Rice "Mock" Waffles................65

Entrees **67-80**

Pizza Pie 68-69

Lasagna...70-71

Chicken Parmesan............................72-73

Italian Meatballs 74

Turkey Veggie Meatballs 76

Lamb Veggie Meatballs 77

Veggie Ground Beef Meatballs 78

Chicken Nuggets 79

Steak Bombs...80

Side Dishes....................................**81-87**

Stuffing...82

Mashed Potatoes 83

Homestyle Potatoes..............................83

Mashed Sweet Potatoes 84

Roasted Sweet Potatoes 84

Quinoa Rice 85

Millet Rice 85

Brown Rice 85

Roasted Squash and Zucchini...............86

Garden Salad with Italian Dressing 87

Pies...**88-94**

Apple Pie..89

Blueberry Pies.......................................90

Traditional Pumpkin Pie with Crust 91

Crustless Pumpkin Pie 92

Apple Crisp 93

Chocolate Mousse Pie 94

Mother Necessity Recipes

Due to the ever-increasing number of food allergies, diabetes, obesity, cancer, and other degenerative and progressive diseases, many people agree that the average diet does not provide the necessary nutrients to prevent disease and support proper brain and body function. *The National Cancer Institute estimates that roughly one-third of all cancer deaths may be diet related.* Nutrition is vital in normal development and function, as well as resistance to infection and disease. Nutrition assists the body's natural ability to heal, and supports both the body and mind.

I have developed the recipes in this book to assist others with eating their favorite foods, healthy. The recipes I have developed are free of chemicals and "common" food allergens. They are designed to provide individuals with optimal nutrition without sacrificing taste. Many people associate food allergies with food deprivation. This does not need to be the case. I have found that all foods can be transformed into healthy foods.

The following recipes have been created using minimal ingredients to ensure proper digestion and assimilation of nutrients. Complicated meals can burden the digestive system and result in incomplete digestion. I have used common ingredients throughout the course of this cookbook to maximize nutritional benefits and minimize preparation and cooking time.

All of Mother Necessity recipes have been carefully formulated specifically for their nutritional profiles; to support proper digestion, blood sugar, and overall good health. All recipes are low in carbohydrates and sugar, yet high in protein, vitamin, minerals, and essential fatty acids.

Most importantly, the recipes found in this cookbook have a purpose—to support and fuel the body. I believe optimal nutrition is required for good health and well-being. Optimal nutrition needs to come from whole foods, and cannot be found in refined or packaged food. Optimal nutrition requires that carbohydrates, fats, proteins, vitamins, minerals, and other micronutrients be supplied to the body in adequate and balanced amounts. These nutrients are vital for proper brain and body function, normal organ development, cell reproduction, growth, maintenance, and resistance to infection and disease.

The recipes in this book have been developed to broaden food selections for people who suffer from food and/or chemical allergies. I do not believe there is one universal diet for everyone. We are all individuals, who require individual nutritional requirements. I encourage everyone to become aware of their *own* body and devise a food menu that is most compatible for their body and nutritional needs.

If I could offer one piece of advice to anyone who is looking to achieve better health, I would recommend whole, organic foods, free of chemicals and contaminants. I also would advise individuals not to limit themselves to one food group. Nutrition should be varied, as our bodies depend on varied nutrients to support optimal health.

Repetitious exposure to a particular food, improper digestion, poor integrity of the intestinal barrier, and chronic chemical exposure are factors that can lead to the development and maintenance of food allergies and intolerances.

Raw Foods

Mother Necessity Recipes offer a selection of both "raw" and "cooked" organic foods. Raw foods are living foods, with their enzymes still intact, and vitamins and minerals in their natural state. Heating food above 118 degrees is believed to destroy enzymes that assist with proper digestion and absorption of food. Cooking is also thought to diminish the nutritional value and "life force" of food.

With the help of a dehydrator (which blows air through food at a temperature of less than 116 degrees) you can cook food without cooking out the nutrients. Best yet, you won't even know you are eating healthy. All of Mother Necessity's "raw" recipes taste like "traditional" treats, yet they have all of their nutrition and enzymes still intact.

Dylan

The following gluten-free/casein-free recipes were developed out of necessity for my son, Dylan. When Dylan was diagnosed with autism I began to do extensive research on sources of common food allergens, chemicals, and toxins and their effects on the digestive system, central nervous system, brain, and immune system. As my husband and I eliminated immune compromising substances (chemicals, common food allergens, nutritionally void foods) and introduced nutrition into our son's body, we began to watch our son strengthen and heal. Dylan's diagnosis of autism was later removed and replaced with a more appropriate label—Multiple Chemical Sensitivity (MCS). Ironically, Dylan's MCS was the underlying cause of his autism. As a symptom of Dylan's Multiple Chemical Sensitivity, he would suffer from typical autistic symptoms when exposed to chemicals through foods, cleaners, medicines, and common food allergens (such as gluten, casein, and soy).

* Multiple chemical sensitivity is often referred to as environmental illness. It is an immune and nervous system disorder that involves severe reactions to many everyday chemicals. The reaction can depend upon the particular organs affected, the person's genetic background, and the specific chemicals involved in the exposure.

Gluten

In recent years there has been growing evidence that individuals who suffer from certain forms of schizophrenia, autism, and multiple sclerosis benefit from a gluten-free diet. It has been suggested that partially digested gluten (wheat protein) and casein (milk protein), with opioid activity, pass through an abnormally permeable intestinal membrane, enter the central nervous system, and affect neurotransmission.

Gluten is a protein from small cereal grains such as wheat, barley, rye, and some oats. When consumed, these proteins are broken down into smaller pieces called peptides, and further into individual amino acids. These proteins can become a problem if insufficiently broken down, and may inappropriately pass through the gut lining and can trigger an IgG immune response.

The immune system calls upon IgG antibodies when unidentified particles or chemicals leak through the gut. This allergic response can occur when partially digested gluten is absorbed into the bloodstream.

The liver is equipped to manage partially digested substances. However, when the liver is overburdened, partially digested substances can pass into the bloodstream where they are not recognized as "self" by the immune system. The immune system will then initiate an immune response against this substance, causing a wide range of physical and mental allergic symptoms.

If a person's digestive system is the least bit compromised, it is very likely that gluten will not be fully digested. Gluten has a tendency to stick to the intestinal walls, and combine with another hard-to-digest protein, casein. Together, these two proteins can form an adherent mass on the intestinal walls, making the absorption of essential nutrients problematic, if not impossible.

Celiac disease is an autoimmune disease that occurs when the lining of the small intestine is damaged from eating gluten and other proteins found in wheat, barley, rye, and some oats. The intestines contain projections (called villi) that absorb nutrients. In undiagnosed or untreated celiac disease, these villi become flattened, and their ability to absorb nutrients properly is altered. This can lead to damage of several organs, and result in malabsorption. Celiac disease can develop at any point in life, from infancy to late adulthood. The only effective treatment is a life-long gluten-free diet.

Only a small portion of gluten-sensitive people will test positive for celiac disease (0.5 percent of the population), while the majority of gluten-intolerant people receive negative or inconclusive results upon celiac testing. New evidence shows that gluten intolerance is around 30 times more prevalent than celiac disease. Up to 15 percent of people, or 1 in 7 people, are gluten-sensitive, and suffer the same symptoms as those with celiac disease. It is estimated that celiac

disease affects nearly one in every hundred people in the United States, of which 97 percent remain undiagnosed and untreated.

Undiagnosed gluten intolerance can lead to a host of health problems and degenerative diseases such as Crohn's disease, diabetes, celiac disease, malnutrition, dermatitis, cancers, neurological disorders, leaky gut, liver fatigue, adrenal disorders, arthritis, malabsorption, auto-immune diseases, *Candida*, and chemical, environmental, and food sensitivity.

The symptoms of celiac disease can vary significantly from person to person. Symptoms may be intestinal or seemingly non-intestinal in nature. This variability is part of the reason the diagnosis is frequently delayed. For example, one person may have constipation, a second may have diarrhea, and a third may have no irregularity in stools.

A partial listing of gastrointestinal symptoms:

- Abdominal pain
- Decreased appetite
- Lactose intolerance
- Constipation
- Nausea/vomiting
- Diarrhea, chronic or occasional stools that float, are foul smelling, bloody, or "fatty"
- Abdominal distention, bloating, gas, indigestion
- Unexplained weight loss (although people can be overweight or of normal weight upon diagnosis)

A partial listing of non-intestinal symptoms:

- Bone and joint pain
- Depression
- Brain fog
- Hair loss
- Mouth ulcers
- Bruising easily
- Fatigue
- Growth delay in children
- Malnutrition
- Muscle cramps
- Nosebleeds
- Seizures
- Anemia (low blood count)
- Short stature, unexplained
- Skin disorders (dermatitis herpetiformis)
- Swelling, general or abdominal
- Vitamin or mineral deficiency, single- or multiple-nutrient
- Bone disease (osteoporosis, kyphoscoliosis, fracture)
- Breathlessness (due to anemia)
- Dental enamel defects and discoloration
- Hypoglycemia (low blood sugar)
- Irritability and behavioral changes

Another, more serious, condition related to gluten intolerance is *ulcerative jejunoileitis*. Patients with this condition usually experience small intestinal ulcerations (breaks on the surface of an organ) and *strictures* (abnormal narrowing of a part of an organ). This can result in intestinal bleeding, weight loss, abdominal pain and intestinal obstruction. People with ulcerative jejunoileitis are also at a higher risk of developing intestinal lymphomas (a type of cancer). While this serious complication of gluten intolerance is often fatal, it is a rare condition. Most forms of gluten intolerance can be successfully treated through dietary changes.

Some sources of gluten include:

- Rye
- Graham flour
- Couscous
- Triticale
- Barley
- Bulgur
- Matzoh
- Some oats
- Malt or malt flavoring (can be made from barley)
- Wheat (durum, semolina, Kamut, spelt)
- Flour, enriched flour, bleached or unbleached flours

Dairy/Casein:

Dairy sensitivity is responsible for gastrointestinal symptoms in millions of people, and has become more noticeable now that thousands of processed foods contain dairy derivatives.

Lactose intolerance is a negative response to the sugar in milk products. Recent evidence indicates that up to 75 percent of the world's population is lactose intolerant to some extent. This means three-quarters of all people have difficulty digesting lactose.

A milk allergy is caused by an allergic reaction to the protein chains in milk and milk products. It is estimated that 50 percent of people suffer from undiagnosed milk allergies. Dairy allergies left unattended can result in malabsorption, dehydration, anemia, osteoporosis, and numerous physical and mental problems. It is estimated, about one-fifth of children with cow's milk allergies have central nervous system disorders.

One of the most important concerns, currently, regarding dairy is the quality. Modern milk has been found to have 400 percent more pesticides than an equivalent sample of conventionally grown grains or vegetables. In addition to pesticides, cows are being raised in unsanitary conditions and being injected with hormones and antibiotics.

Antibiotics are routinely given to cows to treat infections caused by genetically engineered hormones and poor living conditions. The Centers for Disease Control has reported that antibiotic resistance in this country is at an all-time high, and is now a "major public health crisis." The escalating use of antibiotics in dairy production has been blamed for the increase in antibiotic-resistant bacteria. The World Health Organization showed their concern by stating the overuse of antibiotics in beef and milk presents "a growing risk to human health and should be reduced."

Genetically engineered growth hormones are used in cows to increase milk production. One such synthetic hormone is known as Posilac, but it is most commonly known as BGH, rBGH, bST, and rBST. Genetically engineered hormones have been banned in some countries, as they have been linked to various cancers.

Contrary to what we have been taught, milk is not the only form of calcium. In fact, most Asian countries consume little or no dairy, and suffer no calcium deficiency. Recent clinical studies have shown that consuming dairy products at the recommended level does not reliably prevent osteoporosis. A Harvard study revealed that women on dairy-rich diets actually had a higher rate of bone fracture from osteoporosis, than those on a dairy-free diet.

Healthy calcium substitutes include: greens, fruits, grains, vegetables, nuts and seeds. While these foods have a smaller amount of calcium per serving compared to some dairy products, they have more calcium per calorie, and can be absorbed nearly twice as well as the calcium found in cow's milk.

Milk allergies or intolerances have a range of symptoms:

- Iron deficiency-anemia
- Glue ear
- Ear infections
- Runny nose
- Loss of appetite
- Bedwetting
- Chronic coughing
- Constipation
- Asthma
- Bronchitis
- Blood in stool
- Recurrent pneumonia

Ulcerative colitis has been shown to have acute exacerbation with the use of milk. Processed cow's milk has been linked to a variety of health problems, including mucus production, hemoglobin loss, childhood diabetes, recurrent ear infections, heart disease, atherosclerosis, arthritis, kidney stones, mood swings, depression, irritability, and allergies.

Soy

Soy is commonly recommended as a dairy substitute for people who cannot tolerate milk. Ironically, the majority of people who suffer from cow's milk protein intolerance also suffer from soy intolerance. In fact, a growing number of health care professionals are recognizing that individuals who have a previous history

of cow milk protein intolerance have a greater risk of developing soy protein intolerance.

There has been a huge increase in the use of soy in processed foods since the 1990s. It is actually quite difficult to find processed foods that do not contain soy. Interestingly, soy was not used as a food until the technique of fermentation was discovered. Of all legumes, soy has the highest levels of phytic acid. Phytic acid blocks the uptake of essential minerals, including calcium, magnesium, copper, iron and zinc. In addition, soy naturally contains enzyme inhibitors, that prevent enzyme action required for proper digestion. Fermentation neutralizes both phytic acid and enzyme inhibitors, making this process an essential part of soy production.

There Are Many Components To Soy That Would Explain The Increase In Soy Allergies:

• **Genetic Modification**: Soy is the most common genetically modified food.

• **Overconsumption**: Soy is inexpensive, and as a result is being overused in the majority of refined and processed foods.

• **Phytic acid**: Soy naturally contains phytic acid, which prevents the absorption of vital minerals such as calcium, magnesium, iron, and zinc.

• **Toxins**: Soy infant formulas have been known to contain high levels of aluminum. Modern processed soy foods can also contain high levels of MSG, fluoride, and aluminum all of which are toxic to the nervous system. Furthermore, during processing, at least two categories of carcinogens are formed, lysinealanines and nitrosamines.

• **Enzyme inhibitors**: Soy contains enzyme inhibitors, which block the breakdown of protein and lectins. This can result in partially digested food proteins, gastrointestinal discomfort and nutrient loss. It can also encourage leaky gut.

• **Goitrogens**: Goitrogens are naturally occurring substances that interfere with thyroid function and increase the risk of thyroid disease. Researchers have identified that the isoflavones found in soy,

act as potent anti-thyroid agents, and are capable of suppressing thyroid function, and causing or worsening hypothyroidism.

• **Pesticides**: Soybeans can contain high levels of pesticide contamination.

• **Phytoestrogens**: Phytoestrogens are plant compounds that mimic estrogen and can disrupt endocrine function. The endocrine system is instrumental in regulating mood, growth and development, tissue function, and metabolism, as well as sexual function and reproductive processes. Endocrine disrupters are chemicals in the environment that are similar in structure to natural sex hormones and interfere with their normal functions.

In Asia, soy is mostly consumed in fermented form. It is frequently eaten with seafood and seaweed, which provides sufficient iodine to counter-balance the negative effects on the thyroid.

The most important form of soy to avoid is isolated soy protein, which is highly refined and is known to contain harmful nitrites during processing. Isolated soy protein can be found in protein powders, bars, soy milk, baby formulas, and products being marketed as low fat (just to name a few).

Gluten Free/Casein Free Diets:

When I first began the GF/CF (gluten-free/casein-free) diet for my son, I became aware of the challenges that individuals go through when trying to eliminate casein and gluten from their diet. I found the selection of food being offered at the stores to be very limited. When I did find a suitable GF/CF food, I would become frustrated to learn that it contained common allergens that my son would react to. These included soy, egg, corn, and refined sugars.

Another challenge I encountered when changing over to a GF/CF diet was the lack of nutrients in the foods offered. The majority of packaged GF/CF food that I came into contact with was refined and processed. This means that the foods had been stripped of essential nutrients to support proper digestion, brain and body function.

When dealing with any food allergy it is important to know healthy alternatives. Many individuals who are recommended to pursue a GF/CF diet are only being advised to remove gluten and casein; they are not being informed of other dietary factors that can equally impair health.

Important GF/CF Facts:

• **Common Allergens:** GF/CF food can contain common food allergens or reactive food substances such as corn, soy, egg, food colorings and preservatives.

• **Overconsumption:** GF/CF foods primarily use common ingredients. It is important that individuals do not restrict themselves to a certain food group. A varied diet contributes to varied nutrition. Over consuming the same food without any variation can lead to food intolerances or allergies. An individual can become "reactive" to an over consumed food even if it is GF/CF.

• **Refined Carbohydrates/Simple Carbohydrates:** These are not limited to, but include sugar, white rice, and refined flours. These substances can disrupt blood sugar levels, leach precious vitamins and minerals, and cause a host of health problems.

• **Complex Ingredients:** Foods with multiple ingredients can send the digestive system into overdrive and make the digestion process much more complicated and not as thorough. When shopping, always choose foods with minimal ingredients. Eating foods with minimal ingredients will ensure proper digestion and assimilation of nutrients.

• **Chemicals:** Many individuals are not being advised to purchase organic products. The majority of people who have food or environmental allergies typically suffer from an overload of chemicals and toxins in their body. It is essential to eliminate toxins associated with pesticides, fertilizers, feeds and other synthetic chemicals used in conventional farming and manufacturing.

• **Genetically Modified Organisms (GMO):** Many GF/CF foods contain ingredients that are commonly genetically modified. Soy and corn are two of the most widely grown GMO crops. Gene transfers, which are not precisely controlled processes, can disrupt the DNA sequence in an organism and provoke allergies that the human body has never experienced.

• **Additives:** food additives such as colorings and preservatives can have a detrimental effect on mental and physical health. Food additives have been linked to depression, asthma, ADD, ADHD, cancer, allergies, hyperactivity, learning disabilities, headaches, and many other serious health disorders. It is essential for people who suffer from food and/or environmental allergies to choose food that is free of chemicals and preservatives.

• **Lack of Protein:** Many people do not eat enough protein, which slows digestion and helps stabilize blood sugar. Protein at a meal can slow sugar absorption and help prevent hypoglycemic symptoms. Protein intake is the major source of building material for muscles, blood, skin, hair, nails, and internal organs including the heart and brain. When choosing protein, choose sources that are free of chemicals, nitrates, preservatives, colorings, hormones, antibiotics, and pesticides.

Why Whole Foods?

While it is important for individuals to avoid known *reactive* foods, it is equally important to avoid foods that are void of nutrition. Refined foods do not support proper health, healing, and repair. They have no nutritional benefits, and will actually *contribute* to nutritional loss.

I started to incorporate whole-food cooking into my son's diet because I understood that the common ingredients found in the gluten-free products (potato flour, starch, white rice, corn, sugar, and other refined ingredients), would quickly break down into sugar, raising my son's blood sugar levels. This consequently would add additional stress to my son's already burdened liver, pancreas, and adrenals. Simple carbohydrates can also interfere with the utilization of essential fats, causing incorrect or incomplete nerve transmissions.

A diet that primarily consists of simple carbohydrates, refined foods, or high-glycemic carbohydrates

can cause a number of health problems. Frequent consumption can impair and suppress the immune system, cause nutritional deficiencies, disrupt precious blood sugar levels, cause stress to major organs (specifically liver and pancreas), and create a perfect breeding ground for yeast and bacteria. Eating these foods regularly can also lead to many other health disorders such as diabetes, hypoglycemia, adrenal fatigue/exhaustion, and liver and pancreatic disease.

Consuming nutritionally void foods can be especially detrimental to anyone experiencing chronic health problems. Nutrition found in whole foods assists the body with digestion. When that nutrition is not present to aid the body, the body is forced to provide its own vitamins and minerals in order to assist digestion. This can drain an already depleted body of the necessary vitamins and minerals it needs to heal, support, and maintain good health.

Eating whole, organic, unrefined foods that have not been processed or denatured ensures that the body is not being robbed of precious vitamins and minerals. It will also assist individuals in maintaining healthy blood sugar levels.

Best yet, everyone will eat less. We have a desire to overeat when eating refined foods, because refined foods lack nutrients. When nutrients are missing from our food, we instinctively overconsume food to try to obtain the missing nutrients our bodies need.

Why Organic?

Despite the long list of chemicals used in growing conventional fruits and vegetables, as well as the long list of chemicals injected and fed to factory and farm animals, none of those chemicals are required to be listed on the labels or packaging. Therefore, the best way to avoid these chemicals is to buy organic fruits, vegetables, and free-range meats. If you choose to consume fish, choose wild fish over farmed fish and look for fish that has been tested for heavy metals and PCBs.

Chemical exposure has been recognized as a direct link to the development of many allergies and intolerances. It has become widely recognized that once the immune system is no longer exposed to immune-com-

promising substances and immunity is strengthened, food and/or chemical intolerances often disappear. The strong link between chemicals and food intolerances suggests that a reduction in chemical exposures from food and environmental sources can reduce the overall burden on the body, making it stronger and more tolerant.

Chemical exposures are not limited to environmental exposures, and quite frequently are found in our foods. These chemicals include pesticides, hormones, antibiotics, artificial sweeteners, colorings, additives, flavorings, and preservatives.

Individuals who consume organic foods can eliminate chemicals in their diets, while benefiting from additional nutrition. There have been preliminary tests that indicate that organic food has as much as 90 percent more minerals compared to conventionally grown foods. This suggests that organic food provides better nutrition on all levels. With better mineralization comes a greater quantity of vitamins and phytonutrients.

Free Range Meats

Animal protein is a complete protein source, providing the body with all of the essential amino acids. The most important factor when consuming animal products is choosing products free of potentially harmful agricultural chemicals, hormones, and antibiotics. Free range meat is considered the healthiest, as pasture-raising provides animals with what Mother Nature intended—fresh air, humane conditions, and a diet rich in plant foods.

Conventional poultry and cattle farmers use antibiotics and hormones to speed up growth, increase animal size and weight. Farm animals are not only injected with chemicals, they are being fed chemical additives in their daily diets. All of these chemicals, antibiotics, and hormones are then passed on to us when we consume these animal products.

Most poultry producers raise chickens on feed containing both antibiotics and animal by-products. The serious outbreak of mad cow disease (which peaked in 1993) prompted the FDA, in 1997, to ban the practice of feeding meat by-products to cattle or other cud-chewing species. However, there is no prohibition against feeding chickens (and pigs) animal by-products—a source of inexpensive protein. In addition to animal by-products, additives are regularly being used in chicken and turkey feed. Among those commonly used is arsenic. As this hazardous additive is fed to animals, it accumulates in their system, and is then passed on to consumers.

Under current U.S. agriculture policy, the government provides large subsidies to farmers to produce grains, particularly corn and soybeans. Livestock producers like to use corn and soy as a base for animal feed, because these grains fatten up their animals, and save them lots of money. *It is estimated that livestock consume 47 percent of the soy and 60 percent of the corn produced in the U.S.*

Concerns regarding conventional grown grains used to feed factory farms:

1.) **Genetically modified organisms.** Soy and corn are the two most commonly genetically modified crops in the U.S.

2.) **Pesticides.** Conventional grains are sprayed with large amounts of pesticides. These pesticides are known to build up in the fatty tissues of the animals, which are then transferred to the consumer.

Factory beef and dairy cows are primarily fed corn and soy. Cows' digestive systems were not designed for these grains. Consequently, cows can develop severe health problems, which can result in unhealthy meat and milk.

Cows are ruminants, and do best eating what their bodies were designed to digest—grass. Raising cattle on a pasture makes sense for humans, as grass-fed cattle results in meat that is leaner, lower in calories, and higher in omega-3s and vitamin E. Grass-fed dairy products also have five times the levels of conjugated linoleic acid (CLA) than their grain-fed counterparts. CLA is thought to have protective potential for preventing cancer, heart disease, diabetes, and obesity. The general mechanism of protection is thought to come from CLAs anti-inflammatory compounds.

When choosing animal products always purchase organic, free range meats that have not been subjected to chemicals, hormones or antibiotics.

Chemicals

Scientific evidence shows that food and chemicals have a direct impact on our mood, brain function, behavior, and neurological state. The majority of the chemicals that people are being exposed to today are neurotoxins. Neurotoxins directly impact the central nervous system and the brain. Chemicals can be a contributing factor in lower IQs, brain disease, and developmental delays. Chemicals have the ability to disrupt neurotransmitters, hormones, and prevent proper brain development

A *neurotoxin* is a toxic agent or substance that inhibits, damages, or destroys the tissues of the nervous system, especially neurons (the conducting cells of the body's central nervous system). Neurotoxic substances can cause a variety of adverse health effects, ranging from impairment of muscular movement, to disruption of vision and hearing, to memory loss and hallucinations. Some neurotoxic substances can even cause paralysis and death. *Neurotoxic substances* can be found in industrial chemicals, pesticides, drugs, medicines, vaccinations, foods, food additives, cleaning supplies, and cosmetic ingredients.

Evidence is mounting that chemical compounds known as neurotoxins are largely responsible for the fact that one in six children in the US now suffers from some degree of autism, PDD, aggression, dyslexia, and/or attention deficit hyperactivity disorder (ADHD). By avoiding chemicals in our environment and in our foods, we are eliminating debilitating chemicals that can alter and inhibit proper brain and body function.

Food Additives

Food additives are non-nutritive substances added to food to improve appearance, taste, texture and shelf life. Commonly used food additives include preservatives, artificial colorings, artificial flavorings, sweeteners, and stabilizers. Don't be fooled! Just because additives are being used in our foods does not mean they are good for us. Food additives have been linked to diseases and disorders such as diabetes, depression, asthma, allergies, hyperactivity, cancer, learning disabilities, headaches and organ damage—just to name a few. Many food additives have been approved for use, only to be later pulled from the market because they have proven to be harmful to consumers.

Avoidance of chemicals can be achieved by eliminating processed foods and consuming fresh, organic foods. If this is not possible, then the next best thing is to read labels and become aware of harmful chemicals being added to your foods in the form of colorings and additives. These include: blue 1, blue 2, green 3, red 3, red 40, yellow 5, yellow 6, monosodium glutamate (MSG), quinine, saccharin, aspartame, sucralose, butylated hydroxyanisole (BHA), butylated hydroxytoluene (BHT), sodium nitrates, t-butyl hydroxytoluene (TBHQ), hydrogenated vegetable oil, Acesulfame-K, potassium bromate, and all artificial flavorings.

Whether a chemical is believed to be safe for ingestion, or not, it is important to understand that when we put foreign substances into our body, there are consequences. Chemicals alter body function, brain function and can damage major organs. When we eat foods containing chemicals, these chemicals enter our digestive system and contaminate whatever they come into contact with; the digestive system, tissues, brain, hormones and enzymes. Major digestive organs such as the liver and pancreas are extremely vulnerable to chemical damage. Eliminating chemical exposures strengthens the immune system and plays a vital role in eliminating food and chemical intolerances, allergies and sensitivities.

Food Allergies and Intolerances

A food allergy is the body's reaction to a substance in food, which causes the immune system to produce antibodies to attack the offending molecule.

When our son was tested for milk allergies, his tests came back negative. The doctor encouraged us not to eliminate milk products from his diet, despite obvious milk allergy symptoms. The doctor's recommendation was based on the IgE allergy test he performed.

When testing for "classic" food allergies, one of the most common methods of allergy testing is the scratch test. The scratch test is used to reveal IgE antibodies that occur during an immediate allergic response. This method limits testing to only rapid-onset allergies, and misses many other degrees of allergies and sensitivities. A person can experience allergic symptoms either very quickly after exposure (rapid-onset), or a delayed reaction occurring up to seven to ten days later (slower-onset). The slower–onset type of reaction is the more common of the two.

Food allergies are classified as IgE-mediated and non-IgE mediated reactions. IgE-mediated food allergies involve the production of IgE antibodies to certain foods that usually occur immediately after the ingestion of a problematic food. Non-IgE-mediated food allergies involve antibodies other than IgE, namely IgG. There are five major classes of immunoglobulins—IgA, IgD, IgE, IgG, and IgM. Of the five, IgE antibodies are known as the "reaginic" antibody for its major role in investigating immediate allergic responses to foods and other environmental antigens. The other immunoglobulins appear to be more involved in *less-immediate* reactions. Of these, IgG is the most abundant, comprising about 80 percent of all circulating antibodies—making IgG markers an integral part of allergy testing.

Not all food reactions are immune mediated. A *food intolerance* is a common food reaction that does not involve the body's immune system. It is defined as an adverse physiologic response to a food, or given foods. Unlike food allergies, food intolerances can arise from components other than proteins found in food. These can include salicylates, lectins, chemicals, food additives, colorings, or toxic contaminants. Food intolerances typically stem from problems with digestion or metabolism. They are often the result of an enzyme defect or deficiency. The severity of a food intolerance can vary depending on the degree of accumulation in the body. Accumulation can take place when a food is over consumed—added to the body faster than the body can process it. Rotating food groups can be a very effective way of reducing food intolerances. A rotation diet (see "Rotating Foods") is based on eating a particular food once every four to seven days, which prevents individuals from over consuming certain food groups. Rotation has been found effective at reducing and preventing food intolerances.

Food allergies, sensitivities, and intolerances are all equally strenuous on the body. Although there are a variety of tests that are offered to determine allergies, some are not conclusive, and may result in false positives as well as false negatives. Another effective way to find out if a food is causing health problems is to note current symptoms and temporarily eliminate the suspected food source. It is estimated that 90 percent of food reactions are caused by eight foods or food groups: eggs, dairy, wheat, soy, peanut, tree nuts, fish, and shrimp.

Allergies and intolerances are at the root of many health problems. Left unattended, they can deplete the immune system, disrupt proper brain function, and create a host of health problems. When the body reacts negatively to a substance, it puts large demands on major organs and can lead to adrenal exhaustion and fatigue. Symptoms can range from respiratory ailments, skin abnormalities, neurological disorders, and gastrointestinal disorders.

Leaky Gut

Leaky gut is a major contributing factor to food allergies. As the gut becomes more permeable, large food particles are able to pass through the gut wall and eventually into the bloodstream. Once in the blood, the immune system reacts and releases antibodies (typically IgG), to bind to invading food or toxic materials (antigens). With increased gut permeability, greater quantities of antigens are allowed to penetrate the GI barrier, resulting in an overly sensitized, reactive immune system.

When the walls of the intestines become damaged, more openings can develop and allow not only undigested foods, but pathogens, toxins, and other types of waste to pass into the bloodstream. These substances are able to infiltrate the blood and lymph and overload the liver's ability to detoxify. The continued avalanche

of leaking toxins can cause additional chemical sensitivities and environmental illness. Food allergies and intolerances become rampant because the intestinal tract is irritated, inflamed, and porous. The liver becomes overburdened and the immune system becomes reactive. Many autoimmune disorders are thought to stem from leaky gut. It is estimated that 60 to 70 percent of the immune system is located in the intestinal tract and digestive organs.

Some - Leaky Gut symptoms include:

- Asthma
- Weak immune system
- Bloating or Gas
- Mood Swings
- Yeast Infections
- Parasites
- Anxiety
- Fatigue
- Chronic joint and muscle pain
- Confusion, memory problems
- Diarrhea or constipation

Some - Chronic health issues and disorders related to leaky gut:

- Celiac disease
- Chron's disease
- Autism
- ADD
- Schizophrenia
- Autoimmune conditions
- Chemical sensitivities
- Intestinal infections
- Liver toxicity
- Skin disorders
- Irritable Bowel Syndrome
- Colitis
- Malabsorption/Malnutrition
- Food allergies, sensitivities, or intolerances
- Arthritis and other inflammatory conditions

A healthy digestive tract is essential for optimal health and neurological function. Leaky gut can be supported and repaired through nutrition, diet rotation, enzymes, probiotics, and the elimination of known food allergens, intolerances, food additives, chemicals, and toxins.

Rotating Foods

My family has dealt with food allergies through the elimination of processed foods, multi-ingredient foods, chemicals, pesticides, and preservatives. As a preventive measure we rotate our foods to give the body ample time to break down a particular substance. We also prepare our foods in a way that will support proper digestion (soaking and sprouting—see "Soaking Directions" below).

All recipes in this book contain at least three major food groups to assist with rotation. It is has become widely recognized that individuals who eat the same food every day, have a higher chance of developing an intolerance or allergy to that particular food. The tolerance level of an individual can vary depending on the degree of accumulation. This is the result of adding food to the body faster than the body can process it. Rotation gives the body ample time to break down a food before reintroducing it, thus lessening the chance of accumulation. I generally try to rotate foods every three to four days.

Benefits of rotation include:

- Greatly lessens the chances of establishing new food allergies

- Can help treat current food allergies

- Aids in identifying foods that could be causing problems

Blood Sugar

All of Mother Necessity's recipes are designed to support proper blood sugar levels. Refined sugar, flour, and processed foods are sources of simple sugars that are quickly absorbed into the bloodstream, causing a rapid rise in blood sugar levels. Overconsumption of these nutritionally void substances, can lead to poor blood sugar regulation, obesity, hypoglycemia, diabetes, high blood pressure, heart disease, immune deficiencies, and *Candida* overgrowth.

Over time, regular consumption of refined foods and sugar creates a blood sugar roller coaster. This taxes the pancreas, causing it to become very fatigued

and less efficient. The liver, too, becomes fatigued, which can result in poor detoxification. The liver's main function is to make and process new chemicals and to neutralize poisons and waste. Under constant demand, the liver becomes overburdened and unable to keep up with the filtration of other toxins. This can lead to an accumulation of toxins in the body, specifically the fatty tissues.

The adrenal glands also struggle to keep up with the blood sugar roller coaster ride of drastically fluctuating blood sugar levels. Adrenaline is produced primarily when the body is under a tremendous amount of stress. It causes the heart to beat faster, the lungs to take in more air, and the liver to release extra glucose (which is stored as a reserve). Blood sugar fluctuations force the body to stay in "high gear," providing short-term energy and long-term fatigue.

Blood sugar disturbances negatively impact the body and brain and over time can actually damage our organs. Keeping blood sugar balanced is important for overall body function. I firmly believe that proper blood sugar maintenance is essential for proper brain, body, and organ function.

Mother Necessity recipes incorporate both proteins and fats to help stabilize and maintain healthy blood sugar levels. Protein and fats are slowly absorbed, so the sensitive insulin mechanism is less likely to be triggered. Regular meals consisting of some protein and fats keep the blood sugar stabilized.

Eating small meals throughout the day can also help stabilize blood sugar levels. I recommend eating three meals a day, plus four to five small snacks. The objective is to ensure that the blood sugar never drops too low.

Healthy Fats

Healthy fats are the preferred energy source to fuel the body. They are used in the body as a structural component in cell membranes, and as the backbone for hormone-like compounds known as prostaglandins (which help regulate many important physiological functions in the body). Fats also build tissues, enhance fluid metabolism, and direct nutrients to the central nervous system.

Cell membrane dysfunction is a critical factor in the development of many diseases. Particularly harmful to cell membrane function is margarine, vegetable oil, shortening, and other foods containing trans-fatty acids and partially hydrogenated oils. These unnatural forms of fatty acids interfere with the body's ability to utilize essential fatty acids, and are linked to an increased risk of heart disease, diabetes, and cancer.

All cells in the body have a fatty layer that protects them from potential damage. This layer allows nutrients in and waste matter and toxins out. The fatty layer is comprised of essential fatty acids, which cannot be manufactured in the body and must be derived from the diet. If the intake of essential fatty acids is inadequate, the cell walls become more rigid, locking stored toxins in fatty tissues. As fat becomes denser, it becomes more difficult to shift as time goes on. Surprisingly, we need fats to help maintain healthy weight levels. Essential fatty acids are vital for weight management and the movement of stored fats out of the adipose tissues.

Essential fatty acids are invaluable for the production and movement of energy throughout the body. They regulate oxygen, maintain the integrity of cell structure, support the immune system, and synthesize hormones such as prostaglandins, which regulate numerous biological processes, balance inflammation, and influence membrane function.

Every cell in the body needs fatty acids to build new cells. Fatty acids are critical in the transmission of nerve impulses, and for normal brain function. The key is to eat the right *kinds* of fats, such as essential fatty acids found in nuts, seeds, oily fish, leafy greens, grass-fed meat, and unrefined oils.

Nutrition

Foods are the raw materials that provide energy for the sixty trillion cells that make up the human body. Substances found in food have an influence on nearly every health condition. Foods can have a positive impact on the body and support the immune system

to help fight cancer, infections, viruses, and bacteria. Some foods can also negatively impact the immune system, and cause or exacerbate numerous health issues such as cancer, infections, viruses, and bacteria.

Nutrition assists the body's natural ability to heal and supports the body and mind. It also contains energy, and a life force that cannot be duplicated in a lab with synthetic compounds. Nutrition is essential and, in my opinion, is the only way to obtain and support optimal health.

The more we become aware of the amazing miracle of the body and all that it is comprised of, the more we will become aware of our own amazing ability to improve our health by simply making educated choices. We make educated decisions by becoming conscious of what foods we are putting into our bodies and how those foods impact our health. Knowing the difference between good food choices and bad food choices is essential in the pursuit of good health. It is the first step in taking responsibility for our own well-being.

Too many people today make food the main focus of their lives. Many parents find that they cannot provide a healthy diet for their children, because they cannot support a healthy diet for themselves. We are the only culture that views feeding our children healthy as depriving our children. People have become so addicted to foods that they do not realize that it is the additives in the foods that encourage their cravings. The majority of people are so consumed with food that they do not even realize that they are being controlled by it.

I fully believe that food and environmental allergies can be eliminated through proper nutrition and chemical avoidance. We cannot expect our bodies to heal if we are continually subjecting them to poor food choices and chemicals—no matter how many pills or vitamins we arbitrarily take. I have found it to be much more effective to work with the body and to provide it with the nutrients and environment that encourage the body's own natural biological healing processes.

Many of us have been programmed to believe that we can only receive nutrition through synthetic supplements, and have underestimated the power of nutrition in food. *Pills cannot duplicate the complex combination of nutrients found in foods.* Research indicates the natural health benefits associated with nutrition is the result of the synergistic affects of the *whole* food. Isolated nutrients are never found in nature. No nutrient works alone; each is dependent on the presence of others for its best effects. A supplement may contain a single type of nutrient or even several. However, foods can contain *thousands* of nutrients, many of which are still being identified and discovered.

I personally believe that food is the only form of nutrition that the body recognizes, and have a great respect for whole foods, as they have positively transformed the physical and mental health of my family.

Cooking out of Necessity

I knew it was essential to provide my son with proper nutrition, free of common allergens, simple carbohydrates, chemicals, and preservatives. Unfortunately I was having a very difficult time finding healthy versions of my son's favorite foods.

My challenges included:

• **Finding food free of common food allergens**—soy, gluten, corn, casein, and egg. The majority of the food I found contained at least one food group that my son was reactive to.

• **Finding organic, whole grains**—I found it very difficult to find foods that were made with organic, whole grains that had not been refined or processed.

• **Finding food free of preservatives and chemicals**—a lot of the foods I was finding were not organic, and still contained preservatives and/or chemicals.

• **Finding food that was appealing and appetizing**—most of the food that I was coming into contact with looked and tasted quite different from the foods that my family had become accustomed to.

After becoming aware of the challenges of trying to find *nutritional* GF/CF food, free of chemicals and common allergens, I began to cook and develop my own foods out of necessity. I specifically chose ingredients based on their nutritional profiles, and began

formulating foods that would support and benefit my son Dylan's body. *Food with a purpose!* When developing my recipes, I wanted to re-create Dylan's favorite foods. I did not want healthy eating to turn into food deprivation. As a result, I made his favorite foods —Healthy. Dylan can now eat and enjoy foods that his peers are eating, without having to sacrifice his health. Best yet, he is eating food that will support proper blood sugar, digestion, brain and body function.

Today Dylan looks forward to his meals, and we do too. For the first time in our lives, my family is able to sit down at the dinner table and eat the same meal. For the longest time, food was a source of anxiety for my family, ranging from chronic health problems, neurological dysfunction, addiction, self-restriction, limited selection, or simply trying to find healthy alternatives. After years of stress and struggles, I am happy to say that my family is finally in a place where food is no longer an issue. Everyone in our family enjoys what they are eating and looks forward to our meals.

Now that my husband and I have incorporated Dylan's diet (Mother Necessity Recipes), it has become a lifestyle. Organic, whole food cooking has brought us better health, better quality of life, and unity. I feel whole, organic food has been the saving grace in my family's life. Although there are many interventions that are offered in today's world to support good health, I personally feel nutrition and chemical avoidance needs to be the foundation.

Whole Food Preparation

In order to get all of the benefits and nutrients that food has to offer, it is essential to prepare food in a way that ensures proper digestion. This would include soaking grains, nuts, seeds, and legumes before cooking in order to neutralize phytic acid and enzyme inhibitors.

Nuts, seeds, and grains contain *enzyme inhibitors*, which prevent enzyme action. They also prevent the seed from breaking down or degrading. Eating foods with enzyme inhibitors can neutralize the enzymes within our own bodies. This means we can't break down foods that have enzyme inhibitors intact, and these foods, when eaten, can further inhibit us from breaking down other foods in our system.

Enzyme inhibitors can be removed through soaking, which causes them to break down. After soaking nuts and seeds for a minimum of eight hours in purified water, you can access enzymes along with other nutrients that would otherwise not be readily available. Soaking nuts and seeds stimulates the process of germination, increasing vitamin and mineral content.

Phytic acid can be present to some degree in legumes and whole grains. Phytic acid is a potent inhibitor of mineral absorption. It combines with key minerals such as calcium, magnesium, copper, iron, and zinc, preventing their absorption in the intestinal tract. Soaking, fermenting, or sprouting can neutralize phytic acid.

For some individuals soaking or sprouting may lessen their sensitivity or allergic reactions to particular substances.

Soaking Tips

• I recommend soaking nuts, seeds and grains in a glass wide-mouth jar. I use Kerr or Ball glass canning jars. Simply place the grain, nut, or seed in the glass jar, rinse well with purified water, and then soak for a minimum of eight hours or overnight. *Beans, depending on the size, should be soaked up to twenty-four hours.*

• It is recommended to soak items in a dark area, with no direct light or sunlight.

• Sprouting screens are recommended when soaking. They come in three sizes to accommodate the size of the item you are working with. It is important to use either a screen top or a piece of cheesecloth—no jar caps! This is to ensure proper air ventilation. Screen tops or sprouting tops are very useful when soaking, because they make rinsing and draining much easier.

• It is essential to always soak and rinse items in pure, clean water. It is also recommended to use room-temperature water. I use water filtered by reverse osmosis (RO), which is typically room temperature.

• I do not recommend soaking more than one cup of an item, in a jar, at a time. This is because nuts, seeds, grains, and beans expand when soaking. Filling the jar half-full ensures there is enough room for expansion.

• Always try to use whole, unbroken nuts, beans, seeds, or grains. If you find that your nuts or seeds are floating to the top after being shaken or stirred, I recommend discarding floaters, as they could possibly have some degree of damage or rancidity. To remove floaters, take a spoon and skim them off the top.

Mother Necessity Recipes use an Easy Three-Step process:

1. Soak nuts, seeds or grains for a minimum of eight hours.

2. Blend all ingredients in Large Food Processor, Vitamix, Cuisinart Mini-Prep Food Processor or Braun handheld blender.

3. Cook, Dehydrate, or combine the two processes, and enjoy healthy, delicious snacks and meals.

All Mother Necessity recipes use minimal ingredients to ensure digestion is not complicated. Most recipes use similar bases, which are often interchangeable. The following is a list of common ingredients used in Mother Necessity Recipes that replace nutritionally void components that are frequently found in our "favorite foods".

Nuts and Seeds: Replace simple carbohydrates commonly found in cookies, muffins, pies and cupcakes. Mother Necessity Recipes utilize the nutrition and protein that is offered from Almonds, Sunflower Seeds and Pumpkin Seeds.

Whole Grains: Replace processed and refined flours that are typically found in breads, crackers, and pie crusts. Mother Necessity Recipes utilize nutritious gluten free/casein free "whole" grains such as millet, quinoa, and brown rice.

about

Agave: Replaces refined sugar. Agave nectar is a delicious, all-natural low-glycemic sweetener. It is a mineral-rich syrup that comes from the agave cactus. It has a natural and delicious taste similar to honey or maple syrup.

Mother Necessity
Ingredients/Nutritional Contributions

Almonds: The almond is the only nut that alkalizes the blood—all others acidify. Almonds are packed full of nutrition. They contain protein, fiber, potassium, magnesium, calcium, iron, zinc, folic acid, and vitamins B2, B3, and E. Almonds have been found to play an effective role in lowering cholesterol and reducing heart disease. They also contain laetrile, which has anticancer properties. Some people believe that it is beneficial to remove the almond skins for easier digestion; while others believe whole almonds (with skins) provide the most heart-healthy benefits. Please make your decision based on what you feel is most beneficial to your circumstances. *If you decide that you want to remove the skins, then simply pour hot water over the almonds and peel off the skins. Almond skins can also be removed, without blanching, by peeling soaked almonds with your thumb nail or using the thumb and pointer finger to squeeze the skin of the almond off.*

Pumpkin Seeds: Pumpkin seeds contain valuable omega-3 fatty acids. They also supply minerals such as phosphorous, magnesium, iron, manganese, zinc and copper. In addition, they are a good source of protein, vitamins A, B1, B2, and B3, and phytosterols—particularly beta-sitosterol. The phytosterols found in pumpkin seeds make them an excellent part of a prostate health regimen. Eating pumpkin seeds may help provide anti-inflammatory and cardiovascular benefits, lower cholesterol, and prevent certain cancers. Pumpkin Seeds have also been found effective at expelling tapeworms and roundworms. When purchasing pumpkin seeds, look for whole pumpkin seeds free of insect damage. You can also smell the seeds. A musty aroma may indicate that the seeds have gone rancid. Seeds should be stored in an airtight container in the refrigerator or freezer.

Sunflower seeds: Sunflower seeds contain an abundance of nutrients. They are a great source of protein as well as vitamins A, B, D, E, and K, plus calcium, iron, potassium, phosphorus, zinc, manganese, magnesium, and omega-3 and omega-6 fatty acids. Sunflower seeds also contain pectin, which assists in removing heavy metals. Eating sunflower seeds may help provide anti-inflammatory and cardiovascular benefits, lower cholesterol, and prevent cancer. If purchasing or consuming hulled sunflower seeds, make sure the seeds are not yellow or limp. Store them in an airtight bag or glass jar in the refrigerator or freezer. Seeds with shells have an extended life, and can be kept at room temperature for up to a year.

Quinoa: Quinoa is rich in amino acids, and very high in calcium and magnesium. It is a gluten-free grain that provides calcium, magnesium, manganese, vitamins B2 and E, and dietary fiber. It is also a good source of minerals such as iron, phosphorous, copper, and zinc. Quinoa is easy to digest and contains lysine, which is a potent antiviral agent.

Millet: Millet is a gluten-free grain that is easy to digest and highly alkaline. It is rich in magnesium, potassium, phosphorus, and B vitamins. It is also good source of fiber, and offers protection against heart disease, cancer, and diabetes. In addition, it is high in protein, and is considered to be a low-allergy grain. The protein content of millet is generally superior to wheat, corn, and rice.

Brown rice: Brown rice is a quality source of vitamins B1, B2, B3, and B6, as well as manganese, iron, selenium, magnesium, phosphorous, and trace minerals. It contains protein and amino acids, and is recommended as a low-allergy alternative grain. It also supplies gamma-oryzanol, an extract of rice bran oil that has been used to treat digestive, menopausal, and cholesterol problems.

Beef: Beef is an excellent source of protein and vitamins B12 and B6, which are two key vitamins required for proper cellular function. In addition, beef is a good source of riboflavin, zinc, selenium, niacin, iron, and phosphorous. It is best to purchase organic, grass-fed meat. Research is beginning to show that animals raised on a plant-based, grassy diet tend to have fats that are much healthier for the human body (such as omega-3 fats). It has been observed that grass-fed bison, has a significantly higher omega-3 to omega-6 content ratio, than grain-fed bison. Grass-fed meat also has a higher concentration of conjugated linoleic acids, which are fatty acids known to decrease cancer risk, and help many people maintain a healthy weight.

Chicken: Chicken is a very good source of protein, niacin, selenium, and vitamin B6. It is also a good source of pantothenic acid and phosphorous. The healthiest and most humane approach to consuming chicken is to purchase organic, free-range chicken that has been naturally raised.

Lamb: Lamb is an excellent source of vitamin B12 and protein. This vitamin supports production of red blood cells and prevents anemia. It is also important for the normal functioning of the brain and nervous system. In addition to B12, lamb is also a very good source of selenium, zinc, phosphorous, riboflavin and niacin. Research published in the August 2004 issue of the Journal of Neurology, Neurosurgery and Psychiatry indicates regular consumption of niacin-rich foods like lamb provides protection against Alzheimer's disease and age-related cognitive decline.

Turkey: Turkey is a good source of protein, selenium, niacin, zinc, and vitamins B6 and B12. Turkey is particularly high in the amino acid tryptophan, a building block of the brain compound serotonin. Turkey is a lean source of meat, and almost all of the fat in turkey is found in the skin. It is best to purchase organic, free-range turkey that has been naturally raised.

Asparagus: Asparagus is an excellent source of potassium, vitamins A, B6, C, and K, folic acid, riboflavin, and thiamin. In addition, asparagus offers fiber, niacin, phosphorus, protein, and iron. It is also a dietary source of glutathione, which is involved in detoxification and antioxidant mechanisms.

Broccoli: Broccoli is low in calories and is one of the most nutrient-dense foods. It is rich in calcium, magnesium, phosphorus, fiber, vitamin B, and beta-carotene. It is also high in vitamin C and folic acid. In addition, it contains carotenoids and phytochemicals that have tremendous anticancer effects.

Dandelion greens: Dandelion greens offer great nutritional benefits such as vitamins, minerals, protein, choline, and pectin. They are a wonderful source of vitamins B6 and C, riboflavin, thiamin, calcium, copper, manganese, and iron. Dandelion greens also contain compounds that can improve liver function.

Kale: Kale is among the most highly nutritious vegetable. It is an excellent source of carotenes, vitamins B6 and C, and manganese. It contains fiber and minerals including copper, iron, and calcium. In addition, it is a very good source of vitamins B1, B2 and E. Kale is also extremely high in chlorophyll and carotenes, especially beta-carotene, lutein, and zeaxanthin. Studies show that diets high in cruciferous vegetables, such as kale, are associated with lower incidence of a variety of cancers, including lung, colon, breast, ovarian and most recently bladder cancer.

Spinach: Spinach is one of the most alkaline-producing foods. It is an excellent source of vitamins C and K, carotenes, and folic acid. It is also contains manganese, magnesium, iron, and vitamins B1, B2, B6, and E. Spinach is one of the richest dietary sources of lutein, making it an important food for promoting healthy eyesight. Like other chlorophyll- and carotene-containing vegetables, spinach is a strong protector against cancer. Researches have identified at least thirteen different flavonoid compounds in spinach that function as antioxidants and as anticancer agents.

Collard Greens: Collard greens are rich in calcium, vitamins B1, B2, B9, and C, as well as beta-carotene (pro-vitamin A), fiber, folate and manganese. Collard greens supply multiple nutrients with potent anti-cancer properties such as diindolylmethane, sulforaphane and selenium. Collared greens are a wonderful source of potassium, and vitamins B2, B6, and E. They also contain magnesium, protein, omega-3 fatty acids, vitamin B5, niacin, zinc, phosphorous, and iron.

Summer Squash: Summer squash are a subset of squashes, which include yellow crookneck, yellow summer squash, zucchini, cousa squash, and pattypan squash. Summer squash is an excellent source of manganese and vitamin C. It is also good source of magnesium, beta-carotene, fiber, potassium, folate, copper, riboflavin, and phosphorous. In laboratory studies, the juices made from summer squash are equal to juices made from pumpkins, leeks, and radishes in their ability to prevent cell mutations.

Potatoes: Potatoes are complex carbohydrates that contain a number of important vitamins and minerals. They are a very good source of vitamin C and a good source of vitamin B6, copper, potassium, manganese, and dietary fiber. The fiber content of a potato (with skin) equals that of many whole grain breads, pastas, and cereals. Potatoes also contain a variety of phytonutrients that have antioxidant activity. Among these important health-promoting compounds are carotenoids, flavonoids, and caffeic acid. Analysis of Red and Norkotah potatoes revealed their phenolic content rivals that of broccoli, spinach and brussels sprouts. Their flavonoid content provides protection against cardiovascular disease, respiratory problems and certain types of cancers.

Sweet Potatoes: Sweet potatoes are a very good source of dietary fiber and potassium. They are also a good source of beta carotene (a vitamin A equivalent nutrient), vitamin C, and vitamins B1 and B6. Despite having the word "sweet" in their name, sweet potatoes may be a beneficial food for diabetics, as preliminary studies on animals have revealed that they help to stabilize blood sugar levels and lower insulin resistance.

Cucumber: The flesh of a cucumber is a very good source of folic acid and vitamins A and C. The hard skin is rich in fiber, and contains a variety of important minerals including silica, potassium, magnesium, and molybdenum.

Carrots: Carrots are an excellent source of antioxidant compounds, and the richest source of beta-carotene and vitamin A carotenes. They are also a good source of vitamin A, K, and C. In addition, they contain fiber, potassium, vitamin B6, manganese, molybdenum, vitamin B1, B3, phosphorous, magnesium, and folate. Carrots antioxidant compounds help protect against cardiovascular disease and cancer. They also promote good vision, especially night vision.

Apples: Apples are a good source of calcium, magnesium, phosphorus, vitamin C, and beta-carotene. Apples contain water-insoluble fiber and pectin, both of which promote bowel regularity, and help escort toxins out of the body. Regular apple consumption has shown to reduce risk of heart disease, cancer, asthma, and type 2 diabetes.

Blueberries: Blueberries are an excellent source of flavonoids, especially anthocyanidins. These compounds exert exceptional antioxidant activity. Researchers have found that blueberries help protect the brain from oxidative stress. *Based on data from the USDA Human Nutrition Research Center on Aging, blueberries are among the fruits with the highest antioxidant activity.* Blueberries also contain vitamin C, soluble fiber, and insoluble fibers such as pectin. They are a good source of manganese, vitamin E, and riboflavin. Among blueberry varieties, wild or low bush blueberries contain the highest antioxidant power.

Chocolate: Chocolate contains a significant amount of magnesium, and is a rich source of flavonoids and antioxidants. Researchers have long known that cocoa beans contain a class of chemicals called flavonoids, which are also found in fruits, vegetables, tea, and red wine. Previous studies suggest that flavonoids raise levels of HDL cholesterol (the good kind), and act as potent antioxidants, protecting cells from free radical damage, which can contribute to aging, heart disease, and certain cancers. I recommend consuming organic, raw chocolate powder. If chocolate is not tolerated, raw carob powder makes a wonderful substitute that is equally nutritious and stimulant free.

Carob: Carob is stimulant-free, high in protein, and rich in fiber, particularly pectin. Pectin binds to toxins, including heavy metals, and carries them out of the system. Carob is up to 8 percent protein, and contains vitamins A, B, B2, B3, and D. It is also high in calcium, phosphorus, potassium, and magnesium, and contains some iron and manganese.

Greens: The power of green plants are being recognized for their amazing nutritional and healing benefits. Greens are an excellent source of chlorophyll, B vitamins, vitamin C, antioxidants, carotenoids, beta-carotene, calcium, magnesium, iron, zinc, essential fatty acids, vegetable protein, and other phytonutrients. Mother Necessity currently offers *Essential Greens* which is a combination of green grasses, land vegetables, sea vegetables, probiotics and enzymes. It is a complete "super food" that I like to use in some of my recipes to increase nutritional value. Mother Necessity Greens are 100% Organic/Wildcrafted and contain a synergistic blend of all natural vitamins, minerals, antioxidants, essential fatty acids, probiotics, phytonutrients, soluble and insoluble fiber, chlorophyll, amino acids and enzymes.

Coconut Oil: Coconut oil is heat-stable and recommended for cooking. Virgin coconut oil is a healthy saturated fat that is naturally free from trans-fatty acids. It is easily absorbed by the body and used as an energy source. Studies show that coconut oil protects against heart disease, promotes weight loss, and increase the body's metabolic rate. Coconut oil is cholesterol-free, and contains medium-chain fatty acids with 50 percent lauric acid, a health-promoting fat found in breast milk. It also contains another beneficial medium-chain fat called capric acid, which has antiviral and antibacterial properties. It is recommended to use organic, unrefined virgin coconut oil.

Ghee: Ghee is casein-and lactose-free. It is clarified butter, without the lactose and other milk solids. It is traditionally prepared by heating butter, and skimming the foam off the top. It has an excellent aroma and an amazing taste. It has a very high burning point, and doesn't burn or smoke during cooking. It is recommended for high-temperature cooking, and is an excellent addition to sautés, stir fry, and any other high-heat needs.

Agave: Agave nectar is a delicious, all-natural, low-glycemic sweetener. It is a mineral-rich syrup that comes from the agave cactus. It has a natural and delicious taste similar to honey or maple syrup. Its low-glycemic-index rating means it is safe for diabetics and those with hypoglycemia. Agave has a wonderful taste, and can be used in cooking. I particularly like to pair it with nuts and seeds. When paired with nuts and seeds, this low glycemic index sweetener is absorbed even slower into the bloodstream, providing a nice, steady source of glucose for the body. There are many companies distributing agave nectar, I recommend using "raw" agave, which will be specified on the label.

Stevia: Stevia is a natural sweetener extracted from the *Stevia rebaudiana* plant. Stevia is three hundred times sweeter than sugar. Studies have shown a beneficial relationship between stevia and the regulation of blood sugar. Stevia is available in liquid or powder form. Always look for 100% stevia with no additives.

Salt: Common refined salt has been stripped of nearly all of its trace minerals. Unrefined salt is very alkalizing. Adding a touch of salt to cooked grains or meat can restore balance to acid-forming food. Unrefined salt also contains a wide range of minerals needed for optimal body function. Our bodies were meant to function with adequate mineral levels and adequate salt intake. The body uses high-mineral salts to create electrolytes. Electrolytes carry electrical currents throughout the body—sending messages and instructions to cells in all bodily systems. *Salt cravings are a common symptom of people suffering from adrenal exhaustion.* The majority of people with adrenal exhaustion suffer from low blood pressure, mild dehydration, and sodium depletion. The two most recommended brands of unrefined salt include Celtic sea salt and Himalayan crystal salt.

Cinnamon: Cinnamon has health boosting compounds including eugenol, which have potent antiseptic, antibacterial activity. It is also responsible for cinnamons immune-boosting properties and uplifting, reviving effects. In addition, cinnamon contains proanthocyanidins, which have powerful antioxidant effects and aid in stimulating blood circulation. Cinnamon is an excellent source of the trace mineral manganese and a very good source of dietary fiber, iron and calcium. Research indicates that cinnamon has been effective at lowering blood sugar levels and may be useful in the treatment of type 2 diabetes. It has also been noted as a powerful anti-microbial agent that can kill E. coli and other bacteria.

Cloves: Cloves have been used for more than 2,000 years. They have anti-inflammatory, anti-bacterial and antioxidant properties. They are rich in minerals such as calcium, hydrochloric acid, iron, phosphorus, sodium, potassium, and contain vitamin A and vitamin C. They are well known for relieving flatulence and can actually help promote good digestion as well as metabolism. Cloves are regularly used to eliminate intestinal parasites, fungi and bacteria. Their anti-inflammatory properties have been used to help ease the stiffness and pain associated with arthritis. They have also been used for treating a variety

about

of health disorders including toothaches, indigestion, cough, asthma, headache, stress and blood impurities. According to Dr Richard Anderson (Beltsville Human Nutrition Research Center, US Department of Agriculture), compounds found in cloves, like those found in cinnamon, also appear to increase insulin efficiency. Based on Anderson's study, cloves may be important in the alleviation of diabetes and cardiovascular diseases in humans.

Material Resources can be found at the end of this book.

Getting Started

All raw materials for the following recipes can be purchased at health food stores or on the Web (see "Resources"). I do suggest keeping all nuts and seeds in the fridge or freezer, as this will ensure freshness and a longer shelf life. Most nuts and seeds come in plastic bags. I personally like to transfer all nuts and seeds to glass jars and store them in the fridge or freezer (provided the glass is freezer-friendly). I keep all of my nuts and seeds in Kerr or Ball glass wide-mouth canning jars. You can also vacuum-seal the jar with the Foodsaver. The Foodsaver has an accessory that fits on top of wide-mouth jars and vacuum seals the contents in the glass jar. This ensures nutritional value of nuts and seeds, keeps them fresh, and protects them from becoming rancid. You can find this accessory at home stores or online.

Most people are concerned about the cost and availability associated with organic, whole food diets. Talk to your local supermarket and encourage them to carry organic fruits, veggies and naturally raised free-range meats. Many stores are now carrying organic choices and will be happy to accommodate your needs. I also encourage people to try to find co-ops for affordable organic food selections, as well as local organic farms. You can also order your nuts, seeds, and grains in bulk, online. The beauty of working with nuts, seeds, and grains is that they expand when soaked. In some cases they will double in volume, so you literally can get double for your money.

When cooking, I encourage everyone to prepare their foods in bulk. This will ensure that you have enough stock for one or two weeks. I label all my foods and love the convenience of just grabbing my "favorite food" out of the freezer.

What You Will Need

- **Dehydrator.** I use a dehydrator for all of my cookie and muffin recipes. I like to use Excalibur dehydrators. They can be found online (see "Resources").

- **Food processor.** I personally use a twelve-cup Kitchen aid, but any *large* food processor will do. I encourage people to use what they have. After you really start to get into the swing of things, reevaluate your machine and see what your needs are. You will need a large-bowl food processor to mix meatballs, veggies, cookies, muffins, and cupcakes.

- **Mini-Prep food processor.** Large food processors do not work well for *grain recipes*, as the blade is too high and will not effectively grind the grains. As an alternative, I suggest using the Cuisinart Mini-Prep Plus Processor if you do not own a Vitamix. I have specifically formulated all grain recipes to accommodate the limited bowl capacity of this smaller grinding machine.

- **Handheld blender.** When making *raw frostings* and *dips* I suggest blending in a handheld blender such as Braun. The Cuisinart Mini Prep food processor does not effectively grind the small amount of nuts and seeds used in this recipe—while the Braun handheld completely pulverizes these ingredients and gives frosting the smooth texture you would expect from a frosting. *If you do not own a Braun handheld blender, I suggest doubling frosting recipe and using the Cuisinart Mini Prep.*

- **Vita-Mix.** The Vita-Mix is a wonderful, powerful machine. It works great for flat breads. If you have one, I would suggest using it over the Cuisinart mini food processor. Although they are great, they can be expensive. I initially began working with the smaller machines, and as I became committed to making whole foods, I invested in a Vita-Mix. The Vita-Mix can be used to make muffins and works best for grain recipes.

- **Jars and sprouting tops**. Jars and sprouting tops will be needed to soak and drain nuts, seeds, and grains. For jars, I like to use Kerr or Ball wide-mouth glass canning jars. These can be found at your local store, or online. Kerr and Ball jars also fit soaking/sprouting tops. Screens make soaking and draining much easier. Sproutease offers screen lids to fit wide-mouth jars. They are inexpensive and come in packages of three. Each lid is a different size to accommodate small, medium, and large seeds. Soaking/sprouting tops can be found online or at your local health food store.

Guidelines for nuts and seeds

- Always purchase organic raw nuts and seeds. I frequently purchase my nuts and seeds online and have them shipped to my home (see "Resources").

- Nuts and seeds are best purchased in the shell. The shell is a natural protector against free radical damage caused by light and air. In a perfect world, we would be able to purchase nuts and seeds shelled, and then hull them ourselves, as we need them. Unfortunately, I have yet to find a personalized hulling machine, which requires that I continue to purchase my nuts and seeds hulled.

- The key to buying hulled nuts and seeds is to purchase them from reputable companies who have a quick turnover rate, so that nuts and seeds are never sitting too long. In addition, they should be stored in a dark, cool place. I have an extra refrigerator in the garage that I stock my nuts and seeds in.

- To extend shelf life, I transfer my nuts and seeds into a half-gallon, Ball wide-mouth glass mason jar and then vacuum seal it with the FoodSaver compatible attachment.

- Always soak nuts, seeds, and grains for a minimum of eight hours to remove enzyme inhibitors and phytic acid. This will assist with digestion and nutrient absorption. (See "Soaking Directions").

Important Tips

- **Try different things**. Do not be afraid of the food. I encourage everyone to use my recipes as a base. Every-

one has different taste buds. I think it is important for people to feel that they can personalize these recipes based on their own taste and nutritional needs.

- **Salt**. You will find that I use salt in all my recipes. Please feel free to omit if you would like. I think that high-quality salt (Celtic or Himalayan crystal salt) has wonderful healing qualities, beneficial minerals, and an alkalizing effect on the body. I believe it is an important addition to my family's diet. Please feel free to use your own intuition.

- **Agave**. I specifically chose to pair this low-glycemic sweetener with nuts and seeds (to help maintain proper blood sugar levels). I felt the combination of agave with nuts and seeds would provide my family with the steady energy supply needed to support proper brain and body function required for working, learning, growing, and healing.

- **Stevia**. Stevia can be substituted as a sweetener, or used in conjunction with agave.

- **Wet seeds**. Thoroughly drain pumpkin and sunflower seeds before blending and using in the cookie recipes. If seeds are too wet before processing, you may find it hard to form cookies. If you find your seeds are still too wet after draining, you can either dehydrate seeds (after rinsing) for ten to fifteen minutes, or let seeds dry naturally by inverting jar upside down on a dish rack.

- **Soupy cookie batter**. When making cookies it is easiest to work with a batter similar to the consistency of cookie dough—it is much easier to form. If you find that your cookie batter is too soupy, you can simply place batter on a dehydrator tray and dehydrate batter for fifteen minutes or until firm. Then take it out and form cookies.

- **Flat bread unevenly cooked**. If flat bread is not cooking thoroughly on both sides, I suggest placing the pan in the oven horizontally, or rotating the pan halfway through the cooking process. Also make sure you are grinding the grain thoroughly, if grain is not fully ground it can result in unevenly cooked bread. Lastly, make sure that you are not using too much oil. Using too much oil in brown rice or quinoa breads can result in unevenly cooked bread.

- **Making Flat Breads with the Vitamix**. Flat breads are best made with a Vitamix. The Vitamix produces superior bread that is always smooth, consistent and easy to make. When using a Vitamix, you can make multi batches of flat bread with the following formula: 1 cup of grain to every 1 cup of water. For every cup of grain add 1/2 -1tsp. of salt. After processing grain, water, and salt in the Vitamix, measure out 1 ½ -2 cups of batter (depending on the thickness of bread you desire) and add to pan with melted oil. *Always remember to stir batter and oil before cooking.*

- **Storing in glass containers**. I store everything in glass Pyrex containers. You can use unbleached parchment paper on the bottom of the glass container so that nothing sticks. You will also want to use parchment paper to layer certain foods so they do not stick together. This is especially important for meatballs and flat breads (not necessary for cookies and muffins).

- **Freezer bags**. I do not recommend storing food in freezer bags. I try to freeze all of my food in glassware. Plastic can leach and contaminate foods. The more extreme the temperature (hot or cold), the greater the contamination. I only use freezer bags outside the glass container to label and ensure freshness, without contaminating the food.

- **Freezing**. We eat everything out of the freezer. Freezing cookies and muffins actually enhances the texture and flavor of these foods. Cookies are the best right out of the freezer *(they do not taste frozen)*. Muffins and cupcakes can be eaten right out of the freezer, or ready to eat at room temperature within a couple minutes. For my son's lunch I just take cookies and muffins out of the freezer and place them in his snack-size Pyrex container.

- **Rollups**. All flat breads can be made into rollups. Simply cut wider strips. One pan of flat bread will yield two rollups.

- **Reheating**. While I don't encourage reheating cookies or muffins (they are good just the way they are), I do encourage reheating meatballs and bread. Simply place meatballs or bread in a Pyrex glass pan and heat in the oven. The flat bread usually takes five minutes; meatballs usually ten minutes. I recommend letting the flat bread cool before handling. It could break in half if you handle it before it cools.

- **Soaking nuts, seeds, and grains**. Nuts, seeds, and grains will expand when soaked. I suggest soaking one cup at a time (to make sure you have enough room to expand). Your stock will expand as you soak, and in a lot of cases will yield double the amount!

- **Raw cookie dough**. Don't have time to dehydrate? Simply take cookie batter, form into small balls or cookie patties, and freeze. You will have a quick, easy, convenient snack at your fingertips. Cookie dough is great dehydrated, frozen, or eaten straight out of the food processor!

- **Muffins and brownies**. There are three ways in which these items can be prepared:

1. **Cook and Dehydrate muffins.** Cook muffins in the oven at 250 degrees for 1 hour. Let muffins cool, transfer to a dehydrator tray and dehydrate for 4-8 hours at 117 degrees (depending on desired firmness).

2. **Do not cook muffins.** Spoon batter into unbleached muffin cups and dehydrate for 15-20 hours (depending on desired consistency).

3. **Fully cook muffins.** This method is best used when a dehydrator is not accessible. Cook muffins in the oven at 250 degrees for two hours. To firm muffins, place them in the freezer for two hours before serving.

I have provided cooking instructions for muffins using the first method. Please use the cooking or non-cooking method that works best for you!

Cookie Recipes

Mother Necessity cookie recipes are very easy to make and serve as a base to many other recipes found in this book. Mother Necessity cookies are grain-free and do not contain refined sugars. All cookie recipes are naturally sweetened with agave, a low-glycemic-index sweetener which is slowly absorbed into the bloodstream. These tasty treats are low in carbohydrates, yet high in protein, vitamins, minerals, and essential fatty acids.

In order to achieve optimal nutrients from Mother Necessity cookies I have developed "raw" cookie recipes. This ensures that all of the nutrition and enzymes found in these cookies remains intact. With the help of a dehydrator, you can transform your favorite cookies into healthy, nutritious snacks.

If you do not have time to dehydrate—simply take cookie batter, form into small balls or cookie patties, and freeze. You will have a quick, easy, convenient snack at your fingertips. Cookie dough is great dehydrated, frozen, or eaten straight out of the food processor! My family likes these cookies straight out of the blender and will often eat the batter as "raw" cookie dough.

The following cookie recipes are a great way to curb your appetite and maintain healthy blood sugar levels, while incorporating vital nutrients into your diet.

Pumpkin Cookies

These cookies taste like a mild gingerbread or gingersnap cookie.

Health Benefits
Pumpkin cookies contain valuable omega-3 fatty acids, and supply minerals such as magnesium, calcium, iron, manganese, and zinc. These cookies are packed with plenty of protein, fiber, and B vitamins. The carrots in this recipe are an excellent antioxidant source, and contain beta-carotene and high amounts of vitamin A.

What you will need:

2 cups of soaked organic pumpkin seeds. Pumpkin seeds will expand.

> *I find if I soak 1 1/2 cups of pumpkin seeds, I generally will get 2 cups.*

3 organic, washed, and peeled carrots

4 Tb. of organic raw agave

1 Tb. of Frontier organic vanilla flavoring

> *Please be sure to buy glycerin-based vanilla, not alcohol-based!*

1 tsp. of organic cinnamon

1/4 tsp. of organic ground cloves

1/2 tsp. of Celtic sea salt

Large-bowl food processor

Steps:

1) Soak pumpkin seeds for a minimum of 8 hours or overnight. Rinse well (*3 to 4 times*) and drain. *After soaking and rinsing seeds, it is important to thoroughly drain them. It is much easier to make cookies with slightly damp pumpkin seeds opposed to soaking wet seeds. You will find that wet pumpkin seeds will result in a wet batter that is hard to form into cookies — but not impossible!*

2) Place carrots in the food processor and blend until coarse.

3) Combine remaining ingredients into food processor: pumpkin seeds, agave, vanilla, cinnamon, cloves, and salt.

4) Blend for 3 to 5 minutes or until smooth. Pause 3-4 times and take a spoon to scrape any loose ingredients from the sides and below blade. Blend until you have a relatively smooth paste (*may still have some lumps*), similar to cookie dough.

5) After processing, roll a spoonful of batter into your hands and press into a flat cookie. I like to make smaller cookies (*approx. the size of a half dollar*).

6) Lay cookies on dehydrator tray and place into the dehydrator at 117 degrees. I suggest dehydrating these cookies for 15-20 hours if you like crunchy, firm cookies *or* 8-10 hours if you prefer a soft-backed, chewy consistency. The longer you dehydrate, the crunchier your cookies will be. Dehydrate based on your desired consistency.

7) After taking cookies out of the dehydrator, line a Pyrex container with unbleached parchment paper and store cookies in the freezer. Freezing enhances the taste and texture of these cookies. We eat our cookies right out of the freezer. **They do not taste frozen!**

I encourage everyone to use this recipe as a base and modify ingredients based on individual taste buds (more or less agave, water, cinnamon, etc.).

Almond Cookies

These cookies taste similar to a lightly sweetened animal cracker.

Health Benefits
Almond cookies contain protein, fiber, potassium, magnesium, calcium, iron, zinc, folic acid, and vitamins B2, B3, and E. Almonds have been found to play an effective role in lowering cholesterol and reducing heart disease.

What you will need:

2 cups of soaked organic almonds. Almonds will expand.

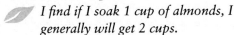 *I find if I soak 1 cup of almonds, I generally will get 2 cups.*

4 Tb. of organic raw agave

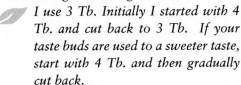 *I use 3 Tb. Initially I started with 4 Tb. and cut back to 3 Tb. If your taste buds are used to a sweeter taste, start with 4 Tb. and then gradually cut back.*

5 Tb. of purified water

1 Tb. of organic melted ghee.

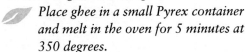 *Place ghee in a small Pyrex container and melt in the oven for 5 minutes at 350 degrees.*

1/2 tsp. of Celtic sea salt

We like this cookie a bit more salty, and use 1 tsp. of salt. Add more or less depending on your taste buds!

Large-bowl food processor

Steps:

1) Soak almonds for a minimum of 8 hours or overnight. Rinse well (3 to 4 times) and drain. *If you would like to take the skin off the almonds, simply place almonds in a strainer and pour hot water over them. Skins should peel off — an additional rinse is suggested.*

2) Place well-rinsed almonds in a food processor and blend until coarse.

3) Add remaining ingredients: agave, water, ghee, and salt.

4) Blend for 2 to 3 minutes or until smooth. Pause 3 to 4 times and take a spoon to scrape any loose ingredients from the sides and below blade. Blend until you have a relatively smooth paste (*may still have some lumps*), similar to cookie dough.

5) After processing, roll a spoonful of batter into your hands and press into a flat cookie. I like to make smaller cookies (*approx. the size of a half dollar*).

6) Lay cookies on dehydrator tray and place into the dehydrator at 117 degrees. I suggest dehydrating these cookies for 15-20 hours if you like crunchy, firm cookies *or* 8-10 hours if you prefer a soft-backed, chewy consistency. The longer you dehydrate, the crunchier your cookies will be. Dehydrate based on your desired consistency.

7) After taking cookies out of the dehydrator, line a Pyrex container with unbleached parchment paper and store cookies in the freezer. Freezing enhances the taste and texture of these cookies. We eat our cookies right out of the freezer. ***They do not taste frozen!***

I encourage everyone to use this recipe as a base and modify ingredients based on individual taste buds (more or less salt, agave, ghee, etc.).

Apple Cinnamon Cookies

This cookie is a wonderful combination of almonds, apples, and cinnamon.

Health Benefits

Apple cinnamon cookies contain protein, fiber, potassium, magnesium, calcium, iron, zinc, folic acid, and vitamins B2, B3, and E. The apples used in this recipe contribute additional nutrients such as calcium, magnesium, phosphorus, vitamin C, beta-carotene, and fiber.

What you will need:

2 cups of soaked organic almonds. Almonds will expand.

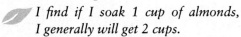 *I find if I soak 1 cup of almonds, I generally will get 2 cups.*

5 Tb. of organic raw agave

1 cup of peeled organic apples

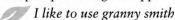 *I like to use granny smith*

2 Tb. of purified water

1 tsp. of organic melted coconut oil.

Place coconut oil in a small glass Pyrex bowl and melt in the oven for 5 minutes at 350 degrees.

1/4 tsp. of Celtic sea salt

2 ¼ tsp. of organic cinnamon

1/4 tsp. of organic cloves

2 tsp. of freshly squeezed organic lemon

Large-bowl food processor

Steps:

1) Soak almonds for a minimum of 8 hours or overnight. Rinse well *(3 to 4 times)* and drain. *If you would like to take the skin off the almonds, simply place almonds in a strainer and pour hot water over them. Skins should peel off — an additional rinse is suggested.*

2) Place well-rinsed almonds in a food processor and blend until coarse.

3) Add remaining ingredients to food processor: agave, water, apple, coconut oil, salt, lemon juice, cinnamon, and cloves.

4) Blend for 2 to 3 minutes or until smooth. Pause 3 to 4 times and take a spoon to scrape any loose ingredients from the sides and below blade. Blend until you have a relatively smooth paste *(may still have some lumps)*, similar to cookie dough.

5) After processing, roll a spoonful of batter into your hands and press into a flat cookie.

6) Lay cookies on dehydrator tray and place into the dehydrator at 117 degrees. I suggest dehydrating these cookies for 15-20 hours if you like crunchy, firm cookies *or* 8-10 hours if you prefer a soft-backed, chewy consistency. The longer you dehydrate, the crunchier your cookies will be. Dehydrate based on your desired consistency.

7) After taking cookies out of the dehydrator, line a Pyrex container with unbleached parchment paper and store cookies in the freezer. Freezing enhances the taste and texture of these cookies. We eat our cookies right out of the freezer. ***They do not taste frozen!***

I encourage everyone to use this recipe as a base and modify ingredients based on individual taste buds (more or less water, agave, apples, spices, etc.).

Peppermint Cookies

These cookies taste like little peppermint patties — best yet, you are sneaking in some greens without anyone even knowing it!

Health Benefits

Peppermint cookies contain an abundance of nutrients. They are a great source of protein as well as vitamins A, B, D, E, and K; plus calcium, iron, potassium, phosphorous, zinc, manganese, magnesium, and omega-3 and omega-6 fatty acids. The use of carob and greens in this recipe contributes additional vitamins, minerals, essential fatty acids, and antioxidants.

What you will need:

2 cups of soaked organic sunflower seeds. Sunflower seeds will expand.

 I find if I soak 1 1/4 cups of sunflower seeds I generally will get 2 cups.

3 Tb. of organic raw agave

1 Tb. of Frontier organic vanilla flavoring

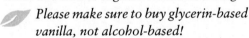 *Please make sure to buy glycerin-based vanilla, not alcohol-based!*

1/2 tsp. of Simply Organic or Frontier peppermint flavoring

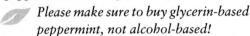 *Please make sure to buy glycerin-based peppermint, not alcohol-based!*

2 tsp. of Mother Necessity Essential Greens or equivalent green powder

2 Tb. of raw carob powder

1/8 tsp. of Celtic sea salt

Large-bowl food processor

Steps:

1) Soak sunflower seeds for a minimum of 8 hours or overnight. Rinse well (*3 to 4 times*) and drain. *After soaking and rinsing seeds, thoroughly drain them. It is much easier to make cookies with slightly damp sunflower seeds opposed to soaking wet. You will find that wet sunflower seeds will result in a wet batter that is hard to form into cookies—but not impossible!*

2) Combine all ingredients into food processor: sunflower seeds, agave, vanilla, peppermint, green powder, carob, and salt.

3) Blend for 2 to 3 minutes or until smooth. Pause 3 to 4 times and take a spoon to scrape any loose ingredients from the sides and below blade. Blend until you have a relatively smooth paste (*may still have some lumps*), similar to cookie dough.

4) After processing, roll a spoonful of batter in your hands and press into a flat cookie.

5) Lay cookies on dehydrator tray and place into the dehydrator at 117 degrees. These cookies are best not over-dehydrated. I suggest dehydrating these cookies at 117 degrees for only 8 hours. The consistency will be similar to a soft, fresh-baked cookie. The longer you dehydrate, the crunchier your cookies will be. Dehydrate based on your desired consistency.

6) After taking cookies out of the dehydrator, line a Pyrex container with unbleached parchment paper and store cookies in the freezer. Freezing enhances the taste and texture of these cookies. We eat our cookies right out of the freezer. ***They do not taste frozen!***

I encourage everyone to use this recipe as a base, and modify ingredients based on individual taste buds (more or less salt, agave, greens, peppermint, etc).

"Green" Carob Cookies

These cookies are very versatile and taste quite mild — the addition of unrefined salt gives this cookie a slight peanut butter taste.

Health Benefits

Carob cookies contain an abundance of nutrients. They are a great source of protein as well as vitamins A, B, D, E, and K; plus calcium, iron, potassium, phosphorous, zinc, manganese, magnesium, and omega-3 and omega-6 fatty acids. Carob and greens contribute additional vitamins, minerals, essential fatty acids, and antioxidants to these cookies.

What you will need:

2 cups of soaked organic sunflower seeds. Sunflower seeds will expand.

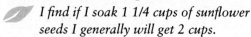 *I find if I soak 1 1/4 cups of sunflower seeds I generally will get 2 cups.*

3 Tb. of organic raw agave

1 Tb. of Frontier organic vanilla flavoring

Please make sure to buy glycerin-based vanilla, not alcohol-based!

2 tsp. of Mother Necessity Essential Greens or equivalent green powder

2 Tb. of raw carob powder

1/2 tsp. of Celtic sea salt

Large-bowl food processor

Steps:

1) Soak sunflower seeds for a minimum of 8 hours or overnight. Rinse well (*3 to 4 times*) and drain. *After soaking and rinsing seeds, thoroughly drain them. It is much easier to make cookies with slightly damp sunflower seeds opposed to soaking wet. You will find that wet sunflower seeds will result in a wet batter that is hard to form into cookies—but not impossible!*

2) Combine all ingredients into food processor: sunflower seeds, agave, vanilla, green powder, carob, and salt.

3) Blend for 2 to 3 minutes or until smooth. Pause 3 to 4 times and take a spoon to scrape any loose ingredients from the sides and below blade. Blend until you have a relatively smooth paste (*may still have some lumps*), similar to cookie dough.

4) After processing, roll a spoonful of batter in your hands and press into a flat cookie.

5) Lay cookies on dehydrator tray and place into the dehydrator at 117 degrees. These cookies are best not over-dehydrated. I suggest dehydrating these cookies at 117 degrees for only 8 hours. The consistency will be similar to a soft, fresh-baked cookie. The longer you dehydrate, the crunchier your cookies will be. Dehydrate based on your desired consistency.

6) After taking cookies out of the dehydrator, line a Pyrex container with unbleached parchment paper and store cookies in the freezer. Freezing enhances the taste and texture of these cookies. We eat our cookies right out of the freezer. ***They do not taste frozen!***

These cookies are also great straight out of the food processor. Simply form batter into a cookie and then place in the freezer. Freeze until firm and eat as a convenient, healthy snack!

"Mock" Oatmeal Cookies

These are an old-time favorite for both kids and adults!

Health Benefits

Oatmeal cookies contain an abundance of nutrients. They are a great source of protein as well as vitamins A, B, D, E, and K. They also contain calcium, iron, potassium, phosphorous, zinc, manganese, magnesium, and omega-3 and omega-6 fatty acids. The carob used in this recipe is up to 8 percent protein, and contains vitamins A, B, B2, B3, and D. It is also high in calcium, phosphorus, potassium, and magnesium, and contains some iron and manganese.

What you will need:

2 cups of soaked organic sunflower seeds. Sunflower seeds will expand.

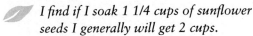 *I find if I soak 1 1/4 cups of sunflower seeds I generally will get 2 cups.*

4 Tb. of organic raw agave

1 Tb. of Frontier organic vanilla flavoring

Please make sure to buy glycerin-based vanilla, not alcohol-based!

1 Tb. of raw carob powder

1 tsp. of organic cinnamon

1/4 tsp. of organic cloves

1/8 tsp. of Celtic sea salt

Large-bowl food processor

Steps:

1) Soak sunflower seeds for a minimum of 8 hours or overnight. Rinse well (*3 to 4 times*) and drain. *After soaking and rinsing seeds, thoroughly drain them. It is much easier to make cookies with slightly damp sunflower seeds opposed to soaking wet. You will find that wet sunflower seeds will result in a wet batter that is hard to form into cookies — but not impossible!*

2) Combine all ingredients into food processor: sunflower seeds, agave, vanilla, cinnamon, carob, and cloves.

3) Blend for 2 to 3 minutes or until smooth. Pause 3 to 4 times and take a spoon to scrape any loose ingredients from the sides and below blade. Blend until you have a relatively smooth paste (*may still have some lumps*), similar to cookie dough.

4) After processing, roll a spoonful of batter in your hands and press into a flat cookie.

5) Lay cookies on dehydrator tray and place into the dehydrator at 117 degrees. These cookies are best not over-dehydrated. I suggest dehydrating these cookies at 117 degrees for only 8 hours. The consistency will be similar to a soft, fresh-baked cookie. The longer you dehydrate, the crunchier your cookies will be. Dehydrate based on your desired consistency.

6) After taking cookies out of the dehydrator, line a Pyrex container with unbleached parchment paper and store cookies in the freezer. Freezing enhances the taste and texture of these cookies. We eat our cookies right out of the freezer. ***They do not taste frozen!***

I encourage everyone to use this recipe as a base and modify ingredients based on individual taste buds (more or less salt, cinnamon, vanilla, cloves, etc.)

Chocolate Cookies

Truly a treat. This cookie will tempt
your taste buds!

Health Benefits

Chocolate cookies contain protein, fiber, potassium, magnesium, calcium, iron, zinc, folic acid, and vitamins B2, B3, and E. Almonds have been found to play an effective role in lowering cholesterol and reducing heart disease. The chocolate in this cookie contributes a significant amount of magnesium, and is a rich source of flavonoids and antioxidants.

What you will need:

2 cups of soaked organic almonds. Almonds will expand.

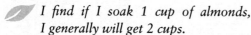 *I find if I soak 1 cup of almonds, I generally will get 2 cups.*

4 Tb. of organic raw agave

5 Tb. of Frontier organic vanilla flavoring

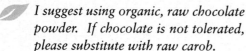 *Please make sure to buy glycerin-based vanilla, not alcohol – based!*

2 Tb. of purified water

3 Tb. of organic, unsweeened chocolate powder

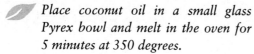 *I suggest using organic, raw chocolate powder. If chocolate is not tolerated, please substitute with raw carob.*

1/4 tsp. of Celtic sea salt

1/2 tsp. of melted unrefined organic coconut oil

Place coconut oil in a small glass Pyrex bowl and melt in the oven for 5 minutes at 350 degrees.

Large-bowl food processor

Steps:

1) Soak almonds for a minimum of 8 hours or overnight. Rinse well (*3 to 4 times*) and drain. *If you would like to take the skin off the almonds, simply place almonds in a strainer and pour hot water over them. Skins should peel right off—an additional rinse is suggested.*

2) Place well-rinsed almonds in a food processor and blend until coarse.

3) Add remaining ingredients: agave, vanilla, water, chocolate, salt, and coconut oil.

4) Blend for 2 to 3 minutes or until smooth. Pause 3 to 4 times and take a spoon to scrape any loose ingredients from the sides of the bowl and below the blade. Blend until you have a relatively smooth paste (*may still have some lumps*), similar to cookie dough.

5) After processing, roll a spoonful of batter into your hands and press into a flat cookie.

6) Lay cookies on dehydrator tray and place into the dehydrator at 117 degrees. These cookies are best not over-dehydrated. I suggest dehydrating these cookies at 117 degrees for only 8-10 hours. The consistency will be similar to a soft, fresh-baked cookie. The longer you dehydrate, the crunchier your cookies will be. Dehydrate based on your desired consistency.

7) After taking cookies out of the dehydrator, line a Pyrex container with unbleached parchment paper and store cookies in the freezer. Freezing enhances the taste and texture of these cookies. We eat our cookies right out of the freezer. ***They do not taste frozen!***

Option: Add 1/2 Tsp. of organic peppermint
flavor to this recipe and you can have yet another
favorite treat!

"Mock" Chocolate Chip Cookies

These cookies look and taste like an old-time favorite!

Mother Necessity chocolate chip cookies contain protein, fiber, potassium, magnesium, calcium, iron, zinc, folic acid, and vitamins B2, B3, and E. Almonds have been found to play an effective role in lowering cholesterol and reducing heart disease. The chocolate in this cookie contributes a significant amount of magnesium, and is a rich source of flavonoids and antioxidants.

What you will need for cookies:

2 cups of soaked organic almonds. Almonds will expand.

 I find if I soak 1 cup of almonds, I generally will get 2 cups.

4 Tb. of organic raw agave

5 Tb. of purified water

1 Tb. of organic melted ghee.

 Place ghee in a small glass Pyrex bowl and melt in the oven for 5 minutes at 350 degrees.

1/2 tsp. of Celtic sea salt

Large-bowl food processor

What you will need for chocolate chips:

1 Tb. of organic, unsweeened chocolate powder

 I suggest using organic, raw chocolate powder. If chocolate is not tolerated, please substitute with raw carob.

1 Tb. of organic raw agave

1 Tb. of Frontier organic vanilla flavoring.

 Please make sure to buy glycerin-based vanilla not alcohol-based!

Steps:

1) Soak almonds for a minimum of 8 hours or overnight. Rinse well (*3 to 4 times*) and drain. *If you would like to take the skin off the almonds, simply place almonds in a strainer and pour hot water over them. Skins should peel right off — an additional rinse is suggested.*

2) Place well-rinsed almonds in a food processor and blend until coarse.

3) Add remaining cookie ingredients: agave, water, ghee, and salt.

4) Blend for 2 to 3 minutes or until smooth. Pause 3 to 4 times and take a spoon to scrape any loose ingredients from the sides of the bowl and below the blade. Blend until you have a relatively smooth paste (may still have some lumps), similar to cookie dough.

5) After processing cookies, roll a good amount of batter (2 to 3 Tb.) into your hands and press flat into a cookie— these cookies are best big!

6) Place cookies on a dehydrator tray.

7) Combine chocolate chip ingredients (*chocolate or carob, vanilla, and agave*) in a small bowl and whisk with fork until well blended.

8) Take a spoonful of chocolate or carob mix and place chocolate dots on the cookies. *We fill a medicine dropper with chocolate/carob mix — it makes great "mock" chocolate chips*

9) After placing chocolate chips on cookies, place cookies in the dehydrator at 117 degrees for 8-10 hours. These cookies taste best when they are a soft-baked consistency. The longer you dehydrate cookies the crunchier they will be! I encourage everyone to dehydrate based on their desired consistency.

10) After taking cookies out of the dehydrator, line a Pyrex container with unbleached parchment paper and store cookies in the freezer. Freezing enhances the taste and texture of these cookies. We eat our cookies right out of the freezer. ***They do not taste frozen!***

Option: If you want to make striped chocolate cookies, simply drizzle chocolate over the cookies!

Breakfast Ideas

There's no way around it—kids love cereal!

As a result, I have tried to come up with a cereal alternative. Breakfast is one of the most important meals of the day. Unfortunately, it is also a common source of nutritionally void substances such as sugar, refined flours, preservatives, colorings, and other undesirable ingredients. These ingredients contain no nutritional value required for a busy day, and can cause blood sugar fluctuations and deplete the body of vital vitamins, minerals, and energy reserves.

The following breakfast recipes are a wonderful way to nutritionally start your day. They contain protein, vitamins, minerals, and essential fatty acids. Best yet, they will not deplete the body of energy—instead, they will provide the body with the support it needs for an active day!

The cereals found in this section can be eaten as instant or traditional cereals. Instant cereal is blended in the food processor, and can be eaten as is, or heated in the oven for 5-10 minutes and enjoyed warm. Traditional "crunchy" cereal is achieved by placing pre-made cookies in a food processor and then topping with one of Mother Necessity's dairy-free milk alternatives.

In addition to cereals, all "raw" cookie recipes can be made into donut holes and dehydrated, to further diversify breakfast options. Simply take cookie batter (see cookies) and roll into donut hole size balls. Then place in the dehydrator and dehydrate for 10-15 hours, or until desired consistency is reached.

Almond Cereal

Packed with protein, calcium, and fiber —
this cereal is a delicious way to start
your day!

Health Benefits
Almonds have been found to play an effective role
in lowering cholesterol. They are also the only nut
to alkalize the blood—all others acidify. This delicious breakfast cereal contains magnesium, calcium,
iron, zinc, folic acid, and vitamins B2, B3 and E.

What you will need for "traditional" cereal:

1 cup of soaked organic almonds. Almonds
will expand.

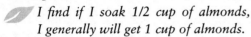 *I find if I soak 1/2 cup of almonds,
I generally will get 1 cup of almonds.*

3 Tb. of organic raw agave

1/2 cup + 1 Tb. of purified water

1/2 Tb. of organic melted ghee.

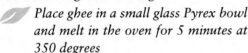 *Place ghee in a small glass Pyrex bowl
and melt in the oven for 5 minutes at
350 degrees*

1/4 tsp. of Celtic sea salt

Large-bowl food processor

What you will need for "traditional" cereal:

1 cup of pre-made almond cookies out of
the freezer.

Dairy Free milk alternative found on
page 43.

Cuisinart mini food prep or handheld
blender.

Steps for instant cereal:

1) Place well-rinsed almonds in a food processor and
blend until coarse.

2) Add remaining ingredients into the food processor:
agave, water, ghee, and salt.

3) Blend for 2 to 3 minutes or until desired consistency is
reached.

4) Pour contents into a bowl and voila, you have instant
cereal that requires no additional liquid. *Fresh fruits
such as blueberries or raspberries are very compatible
with this cereal—feel free to improvise!*

5) Cereal can be warmed in the oven for 5-10 minutes at
250 degrees, or served straight from the blender.

When making instant cereal, I suggest using all of the
contents at once. This recipe does not keep well!

Steps for traditional cereal:

1) Take one cup of pre-made almond cookies out of the
freezer and place in Cuisinart mini food processor
or Braun handheld blender. Blend until cookies are
coarse.

2) Combine cookies with dairy-free milk alternative and
you have quick, convenient cookie cereal!

I encourage everyone to use this recipe as a base and
modify ingredients based on individual taste buds
(more or less ghee, agave, water, etc.).

Apple Cinnamon Cereal

This cereal is wonderful way to enjoy the delicious combination of cinnamon and apple without the addition of refined ingredients.

Health Benefits
This breakfast cereal contains protein, fiber, potassium, magnesium, calcium, iron, zinc, folic acid, and vitamins B2, B3, and E. The apples in this recipe contribute additional nutrients such as calcium, magnesium, phosphorus, vitamin C, beta-carotene, and fiber.

What you will need for "instant" cereal:

1 cup of soaked organic almonds. Almonds will expand.
> *I find if I soak 1/2 cup of almonds, I generally will get 1 cup of almonds.*

2 Tb. of organic raw agave

1/2 cup peeled organic apple
> *I like to use granny smith*

1 tsp. of organic cinnamon

1/4 tsp. of organic cloves

1/4 tsp. of organic unrefined melted coconut oil.
> *Melt coconut oil in a small glass Pyrex bowl in the oven*

1/8 tsp. of Celtic sea salt

1/2 tsp. of freshly squeezed organic lemon

1/4 cup of purified water

Large food processor

What you will need for "traditional" cereal:

1 cup of pre-made apple cinnamon cookies out of the freezer.

Dairy Free milk alternative found on page 43.

Cuisinart mini food prep or handheld blender.

Steps for instant cereal:

1) Place well-rinsed almonds in a food processor and blend until coarse.

2) Add remaining ngredients into the food processor: agave, apples, cinnamon, cloves, coconut oil, lemon juice, salt, water and vanilla.

3) Blend for 2 to 3 minutes or until desired consistency is reached.

4) Pour contents into a bowl and voila, you have instant cereal that requires no additional liquid.

5) Cereal can be warmed in the oven for 5-10 minutes at 250 degrees, or served straight from the blender.

When making instant cereal, I suggest using all of the contents at once. This recipe does not keep well!

Steps for traditional cereal

1) Take one cup of pre-made apple cinnamon cookies out of the freezer and place in Cuisinart mini food processor or Braun handheld blender. Blend until cookies are coarse.

2) Combine cookies with dairy-free milk alternative and you have quick, convenient cookie cereal!

I encourage everyone to use this recipe as a base and modify ingredients based on individual taste buds (more or less apples, agave, water, etc.).

"Mock" Oatmeal Cereal

This is an excellent alternative to an old-time favorite!

Health Benefits

This breakfast cereal contains an abundance of nutrients. It is a great source of protein as well as vitamins A, B, D, E, and K. It also contains calcium, iron, potassium, phosphorous, zinc, manganese, magnesium, and omega-3 and omega-6 fatty acids.

What you will need for "instant" cereal:

1 cup of soaked organic sunflower seeds. Sunflower seeds will expand.

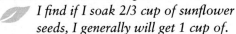 *I find if I soak 2/3 cup of sunflower seeds, I generally will get 1 cup of.*

2 Tb. of organic raw agave

1/2 Tb. of raw carob powder

1/2 Tb. of Frontier organic vanilla flavoring.
Please make sure to buy glycerin-based vanilla, not alcohol-based!

1/2 tsp. of organic cinnamon

1/8 tsp. of organic cloves

1/4 cup of purified water

Large-bowl food processor

What you will need for "traditional" cereal:

1 cup of pre-made oatmeal cookies out of the freezer.

Dairy Free milk alternative found on page 43.

Cuisinart mini food prep or handheld blender.

Steps for instant cereal:

1) Place all ingredients in the food processor: agave, vanilla, carob, cinnamon, cloves, sunflower seeds, vanilla, and water

2) Blend for 2 to 3 minutes or until desired consistency is reached.

3) Pour contents into a bowl and voila, you have instant cereal that requires no additional liquid.

4) Cereal can be warmed in the oven for 5-10 minutes at 250 degrees, or served straight from the blender.

When making instant cereal, I suggest using all of the contents at once. This recipe does not keep well!

Steps for traditional cereal

1) Take one cup of pre-made oatmeal cookies out of the freezer and place in Cuisinart mini food processor or Braun handheld blender. Blend until cookies are coarse.

2) Combine cookies with dairy-free milk alternative and you have quick, convenient cookie cereal!

I encourage everyone to use this recipe as a base and modify ingredients based on individual taste buds (more or less spices, agave, water, etc.).

Pumpkin Spice Cereal

The combination of pumpkin and spice makes this breakfast item a perfect way to start your day!

Health Benefits
This breakfast treat contains valuable omega-3 fatty acids, and supplies minerals such as magnesium, calcium, iron, manganese, and zinc. This cereal is packed with plenty of protein, fiber, and B vitamins. The carrots used in this recipe are an excellent antioxidant source, and contain beta-carotene and high amounts of vitamin A.

What you will need for instant cereal:

1 cup of soaked organic pumpkin seeds. Pumpkin seeds will expand.

 I find if I soak 3/4 cups of pumpkin seeds I generally will get 1 cup.

1 1/2 organic carrots (or 1 cup)

3 Tb. of organic raw agave

1 Tb. of Frontier organic vanilla flavoring

 Please make sure to buy glycerin-based vanilla, not alcohol-based!

1 tsp. of organic cinnamon

1/4 tsp. of organic ground cloves

1/4 cup of purified water

Large-bowl food processor

What you will need for "traditional" cereal:

1 cup of pre-made pumpkin cookies out of the freezer

Dairy Free milk alternative found on page 43.

Cuisinart mini food prep or handheld blender.

Steps for instant cereal:

1) Place carrots in food processor and blend until coarse.

2) Add remaining ingredients into the food processor: agave, vanilla, water, cinnamon, and cloves.

3) Blend for 2 to 3 minutes or until desired consistency is reached.

4) Pour contents into a bowl and voila, you have instant cereal that requires no additional liquid.

5) Cereal can be warmed in the oven for 5-10 minutes at 250 degrees, or served straight from the blender. *My family likes to add 1/2 cup of peeled and diced organic apples to this cereal right before warming!*

When making instant cereal, I suggest using all of the contents at once. This recipe does not keep well!

Steps for traditional cereal:

1) Take one cup of pre-made pumpkin cookies out of the freezer and place in Cuisinart mini food processor or Braun hand blender until cookies are coarse.

2) Combine cookies with dairy-free milk alternative and you have quick, convenient cookie cereal!

I encourage everyone to use this recipe as a base and modify ingredients based on individual taste buds (more or less spices, agave, water, etc.).

Chocolate Cereal

Truly a treat that you do not have to feel guilty about!

Health Benefits
This breakfast cereal contains protein, fiber, potassium, magnesium, calcium, iron, zinc, folic acid, and vitamins B2, B3, and E. The cholcolate used in this recipe contributes a significant amount of magnesium, and is a rich source of flavonoids and antioxidants.

What you will need for "traditional" cereal:

1 cup of soaked organic almonds. Almonds will expand.

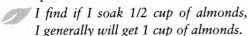 *I find if I soak 1/2 cup of almonds, I generally will get 1 cup of almonds.*

2 Tb. of organic raw agave

3 Tb. of Frontier organic vanilla

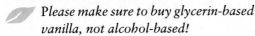 *Please make sure to buy glycerin-based vanilla, not alcohol-based!*

2 Tb. of organic, unsweetened chocolate powder

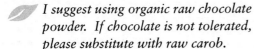 *I suggest using organic raw chocolate powder. If chocolate is not tolerated, please substitute with raw carob.*

1/8 tsp. of Celtic sea salt

1/4 tsp. of organic unrefined coconut oil

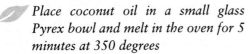 *Place coconut oil in a small glass Pyrex bowl and melt in the oven for 5 minutes at 350 degrees*

Large-bowl food processor

What you will need for "traditional" cereal:

1 cup of pre-made chocolate cookies out of the freezer.

Dairy Free milk alternative found on page 43.

Cuisinart mini food prep or handheld blender.

Steps for instant cereal:

1) Place well-rinsed almonds in a food processor and blend until coarse.

2) Add remaining ingredients into the food processor: agave, water, vanilla, chocolate, water, coconut oil and salt.

3) Blend for 2 to 3 minutes or until desired consistency is reached.

4) Pour contents into a bowl and voila, you have instant cereal that requires no additional liquid.

5) Cereal can be warmed in the oven for 5-10 minutes at 250 degrees, or served straight from the blender.

When making instant cereal, I suggest using all of the contents at once. This recipe does not keep well!

Steps for traditional cereal:

1) Take one cup of pre-made chocolate cookies out of the freezer and place in Cuisinart mini food processor or Braun hand blender until cookies are coarse.

2) Combine cookies with dairy-free milk alternative and you have quick, convenient cookie cereal!

I encourage everyone to use this recipe as a base and modify ingredients based on individual taste buds (more or less chocolate, agave, water, etc.).

Mother Necesssity Milk Alternatives

The following recipes are milk substitutes that have been developed for people who can not tolerate dairy or soy.

Dairy sensitivity is responsible for gastrointestinal symptoms in millions of people, and has become more noticeable now that thousands of processed foods contain dairy derivatives.

Lactose intolerance is a negative response to the sugar in milk products. Recent evidence indicates that up to 75 percent of the world's population is lactose intolerant to some extent. This means three-quarters of all people have difficulty digesting lactose.

Soy is commonly recommended as a dairy substitute for people who cannot tolerate milk. Ironically, the majority of people who suffer from cow's milk protein intolerance also suffer from soy intolerance. In fact, a growing number of health care professionals are recognizing that individuals who have a previous history of cow milk protein intolerance have a greater risk of developing soy protein intolerance.

Contrary to what we have been taught, milk is not the only form of calcium. In fact, most Asian countries consume little or no dairy, and suffer no calcium deficiency. Recent clinical studies have shown that consuming dairy products at the recommended level does not reliably prevent osteoporosis. A Harvard study revealed that women on dairy-rich diets actually had a higher rate of bone fracture from osteoporosis, than those on a dairy-free diet.

Healthy calcium substitutes include: greens, fruits, grains, vegetables, nuts and seeds. While these foods have a smaller amount of calcium per serving compared to some dairy products, they have more calcium per calorie, and can be absorbed nearly twice as well as the calcium found in cow's milk.

A handheld blender, Cuisinart mini food processor, or a Vitamix can be used to make the following recipes. Please note, while the smaller machines are effective, the Vitamix is a superior machine.

Milk Alternatives

Almond Milk

Health Benefits

This milk is delicious and rich in protein, fiber, magnesium, calcium, folic acid, and vitamins B2 and B3.

Place the following ingredients in a Cuisinart mini food processor or Vitamix.

   1/4 cup of soaked organic almonds

   1 cup of purified water

   1 tsp. of organic raw agave

   1/2 tsp. of Frontier organic vanilla flavoring

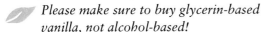 *Please make sure to buy glycerin-based vanilla, not alcohol-based!*

Blend until all ingredients are in liquid form.

Pour ingredients through a cheese cloth or fine strainer before serving.

Probiotic Milk

Health Benefits

This milk helps to reestablish the normal bacterial population in the gut.

Place the following ingredients in a Cuisinart mini food processor or Vitamix.

   2 caps or scoops of a good quality probiotic

   1/2 cup of purified water

   1 small scoop of stevia (*scooper comes with some brands of stevia*), or to taste.

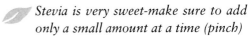 *Stevia is very sweet-make sure to add only a small amount at a time (pinch)*

   1/4 tsp. of melted organic unrefined coconut oil

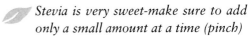 *If you really like the taste of coconut you can use 1/2 Tsp.*

Blend until all ingredients are thoroughly mixed.

Sunflower Seed Milk

Health Benefits

This milk is a great source of protein as well as vitamins A, B, D, E, K, and calcium, iron, zinc, and magnesium.

Place the following ingredients in a Cuisinart mini food processor or Vitamix.

   1/4 cup of soaked organic sunflower seeds

   1 cup of purified water

   1 tsp. of organic raw agave

1 tsp. of Frontier organic vanilla flavoring

Please make sure to buy glycerin-based vanilla, not alcohol-based!

Blend until all ingredients are in liquid form.

Pour ingredients through a cheese cloth or fine strainer before serving.

Muffins, Cupcakes And Brownies

The following recipes are very easy to make and offer a healthy alternative to a once unhealthy indulgence. All recipes in this section are very versatile and can be prepared as muffins and later topped with raw frostings to make cupcakes. Now everyone can enjoy muffins, brownies, and even cupcakes while benefiting from the nutrition that these tastey treats have to offer!

I specifically chose to pair agave with nuts and seeds, as the combination of agave (a low-glycemic-index sweetener) is a wonderful match with nuts and seeds (which contain protein and fats that slow the release of sugars). I felt the combination of these ingredients would support proper blood sugar while providing key vitamins, minerals, and essential fatty acids.

THERE ARE THREE WAYS IN WHICH THESE ITEMS CAN BE PREPARED:

1) **Cook and Dehydrate muffins**. Cook muffins in the oven at 250 degrees for 1 hour. Let muffins cool and then transfer to a dehydrator tray and dehydrate for 4-8 hours at 117 degrees (depending on desired firmness).

2) **Do not cook muffins.** Spoon batter into unbleached muffin cups and dehydrate for 15-20 hours (depending on desired consistency).

3) **Fully cook muffins.** This method is best used when a dehydrator is not accessible. Cook muffins in the oven at 250 degrees for two hours. To firm muffins, I suggest placing them in the freezer for two hours before serving.

For this section, I have utilized the First Preparation Method which incorporates baking the muffins at 250 degrees and then dehydrating. I encourage everyone to use the method they feel will meet their nutritional needs and desired consistency.

Please note that exclusively dehydrating muffins provides treats that are just as delicious, while preserving vital nutrients and enzymes.

Golden Muffins or Cupcakes

These muffins taste like slightly sweetened white refined cake. Fresh blueberries or other berries can be added to batter to further compliment this recipe as a muffin.

Health Benefits

These muffins contain protein, fiber, potassium, magnesium, calcium, iron, zinc, folic acid, and vitamins B2, B3, and E. Almonds have been found to play an effective role in lowing cholesterol and reducing heart disease. They also are very alkalizing.

What you will need: *I suggest doubling this recipe*

1 cup of soaked organic almonds. Almonds will expand.

 I double this recipe and make 2 batches for a total of 12 muffins. I find if I soak 1 cup of almonds, I generally will get 2 cups.

3 Tb. of organic raw agave

 I Initially started with 3 Tb. and cut back to 2 Tb. If your taste buds are used to a sweeter taste, start with 3 Tb. and then gradually cut back

1/2 cup of purified water

1/2 Tb. of organic melted ghee.

 Place ghee in a small glass Pyrex bowl and melt in the oven for 5 minutes at 350 degrees.

1/4 tsp. of Celtic sea salt

Unbleached baking cups

 I use Beyond Gourmet or If You Care brands, found in health food stores.

Large Glass Pyrex pan (9 x 13 in.)

Large-bowl food processor

Steps:

1) Soak almonds for a minimum of 8 hours or overnight. Rinse well (*3 to 4 times*) and drain. *If you would like to take the skin off the almonds, simply place almonds in a strainer and pour hot water over them. Skins should peel off — an additional rinse is suggested.*

2) Preheat oven to 250 degrees.

3) Place almonds in food processor and blend until coarse.

4) Add remaining ingredients to food processor: agave, water, ghee, and salt.

5) Blend for 2 to 3 minutes. Pause 2-3 times using a spoon to scrape any loose ingredients from the sides of the bowl and under the blade. Blend until you have a relatively smooth batter.

6) Spoon your batter into the unbleached baking cups, and place baking cups in a Pyrex pan. A typical batch yields 6 muffins. *I like to double my recipe and make 12 muffins at a time.*

7) Place Pyrex pan in the oven and cook muffins for 1 hour. Then transfer muffins to dehydrator tray and dehydrate for an additional 4-8 hours at 117 degrees. *The longer you dehydrate the muffins, the firmer they will be (freezing also firms muffins).*

8) When muffins are done, line a Pyrex container with unbleached parchment paper and layer the muffins. I store muffins in the freezer. I do not recommend reheating muffins—they are very good right out of the freezer, and thaw in a matter of minutes at room temperature.

Cupcakes:

 Top these versatile muffins with raw frosting (*see "Raw Frostings" section*) and you have a wonderful, nutritious cupcake. *I will often make raw frostings and keep them in the freezer. I like to pull out frosting and top my muffins as a quick and easy treat!*

Apple Cinnamon Muffins

These muffins taste just like the ones "Grandma made", without all of the refined ingredients and sugar.

Health Benefits
It is hard to believe these delicious muffins contain protein, fiber, potassium, magnesium, calcium, iron, zinc, folic acid, and vitamins B2, B3, and E. The apples used in this recipe contribute additional nutrients such as calcium, magnesium, phosphorus, vitamin C, beta-carotene, and fiber.

What you will need: *I suggest doubling this recipe*

1 cup of organic soaked almonds. Almonds will expand.

 I double this recipe and make 2 batches for a total of 12 muffins.

I find if I soak 1 cup of almonds I generally will get 2 cups.

4 Tb. of organic raw agave

1/4 cup of purified water

1/2 tsp. of organic unrefined coconut oil.

 Place coconut oil in a small Pyrex bowl and melt in the oven for 5 minutes at 350 degree.

1/4 tsp. of organic cloves

1 tsp. of organic cinnamon

1/2 tsp. of freshly squeezed organic lemon

1/2 cup of peeled and diced organic apple
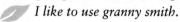 *I like to use granny smith.*

1/8 tsp. of Celtic sea salt

Unbleached baking cups
 I use Beyond Gourmet or If You Care brands, found in health food stores.

Large Glass Pyrex pan (9 x 13 in.)

Large-bowl food processor

Steps:

1) Soak almonds for a minimum of 8 hours or overnight. Rinse well (*3 to 4 times*) and drain. *If you would like to take the skin off the almonds, simply place almonds in a strainer and pour hot water over them. Skins should peel off — an additional rinse is suggested.*

2) Preheat oven to 250 degrees.

3) Place almonds in food processor and blend until coarse.

4) Combine remaining ingredients: coconut oil, water, agave, lemon juice, cinnamon, cloves, apples and salt.

5) Blend for 2 to 3 minutes. Pause 2-3 times using a spoon to scrape any loose ingredients from the sides of the bowl and under the blade. Blend until you have a relatively smooth batter.

6) Spoon batter into the unbleached baking cups and place baking cups in a Pyrex glass pan. A typical batch yields 6 muffins. *I like to double my recipe and make 12 muffins at a time.*

7) Place Pyrex pan in the oven and cook muffins for 1 hour. Then transfer muffins to dehydrator tray and dehydrate for an additional 4-8 hours at 117 degrees. *The longer you dehydrate the muffins, the firmer they will be (freezing also firms muffins).*

8) When muffins are done, line a Pyrex container with unbleached parchment paper and layer the muffins. I store muffins in the freezer. I do not recommend reheating muffins — they are very good right out of the freezer. They thaw in a matter of minutes at room temperature.

I encourage everyone to use this recipe as a base and modify ingredients based on individual taste buds (more or less spices, agave, apples, etc.).

Pumpkin Muffins

Pumpkin and spice and all things nice!

Health Benefits

These scrumptious muffins contain valuable omega-3 fatty acids, and supply minerals such as magnesium, calcium, iron, manganese, and zinc. This recipe is packed with plenty of protein, fiber, and B vitamins. The carrots used in this recipe are an excellent antioxidant source, and contain beta-carotene and high amounts of vitamin A.

What you will need: *I suggest doubling this recipe*

1 cup of soaked organic pumpkin seeds. Pumpkin seeds will expand.

 I double this recipe and make 2 batches for a total of 12 muffins.
I find if I soak 1 1/2 cups of pumpkin seeds, I generally will get 2 cups

1 1/2 organic peeled carrots (or 1 cup)

4 Tb. of organic raw agave

1/3 cup of purified water

1 Tb. of Frontier organic vanilla flavoring
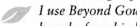 *Please make sure to buy glycerin-based vanilla, not alcohol-based!*

1 tsp. of organic cinnamon

1/4 tsp. of organic cloves

Unbleached baking cups
I use Beyond Gourmet or If You Care brands, found in health food stores.

Large Glass Pyrex pan (9 x 13 in.)

Large-bowl food processor

Steps:

1) Soak pumpkin seeds for a minimum of 8 hours or overnight. Rinse well (*3 to 4 times*) and drain.

2) Preheat oven to 250 degrees.

3) Place carrots in food processor and blend until coarse.

4) Add remaining ingredients to food processor: seeds, agave, water, vanilla, cinnamon, and cloves.

5) Blend for 2 to 3 minutes. Pause 2-3 times using a spoon to scrape any loose ingredients from the sides of the bowl and under the blade. Blend until you have a relatively smooth batter.

6) Spoon your batter into the unbleached baking cups, and place baking cups in a Pyrex pan. A typical batch yields 6 muffins. *I like to double my recipe and make 12 muffins at a time.*

7) Place Pyrex pan in the oven and cook muffins for 1 hour. Then transfer muffins to dehydrator tray and dehydrate for an additional 4-8 hours at 117 degrees. *The longer you dehydrate the muffins, the firmer they will be (freezing also firms muffins).*

8) When muffins are done, line a Pyrex container with unbleached parchment paper and layer the muffins. I store muffins in the freezer. I do not recommend reheating muffins—they are very good right out of the freezer. They thaw in a matter of minutes at room temperature.

Cupcakes:

 Top this savory muffin with vanilla frosting (see "Raw Frostings" section) and you have delicious, carrot cake cupcakes. *I will often make raw frostings and keep them in the freezer. I like to pull out frosting and top my muffins as a quick and easy treat!*

"Green" Carob Muffins

Don't let the name fool you — this recipe makes a yummy muffin and a delicious cupcake. Despite the name, this muffin is not green once cooked. It has a mild flavor, and tastes similar to a lightly sweetened bran muffin.

Health Benefits
This delicious muffin is a great source of protein as well as vitamins A, B, D, E, and K. It is also a wonderful source of calcium, iron, potassium, phosphorous, zinc, manganese, magnesium, and omega-3 and omega-6 fatty acids. The addition of carob and greens contributes additional nutrients such as vitamins, minerals, essential fatty acids, protein and antioxidants.

What you will need: *I suggest doubling this recipe*

1 cup of soaked organic sunflower seeds. Sunflower seeds will expand.

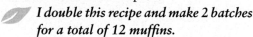
I double this recipe and make 2 batches for a total of 12 muffins.
I find if I soak 1 1/4 cups of sunflower seeds, I generally will get 2 cups.

3 Tb. of organic raw agave

1 Tb. of Frontier organic vanilla flavoring

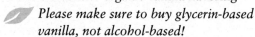
Please make sure to buy glycerin-based vanilla, not alcohol-based!

1/3 cup of purified water

2 tsp. of Mother Necessity Essential Greens or equivalent green powder

2 Tb. of raw carob powder

Unbleached baking cups

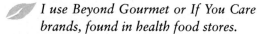
I use Beyond Gourmet or If You Care brands, found in health food stores.

Large Glass Pyrex pan (9 x 13 in.)

Optional – Add 1/4 tsp. of peppermint to make peppermint muffins

Steps:

1) Soak sunflower seeds for a minimum of 8 hours or overnight. Rinse well (*3 to 4 times*) and drain.

2) Preheat oven to 250 degrees.

3) Place all ingredients in the food processor: sunflower seeds, agave, vanilla, greens, carob and water

4) Blend for 2 to 3 minutes. Pause 2-3 times using a spoon to scrape any loose ingredients from the sides of the bowl and under the blade. Blend until you have a relatively smooth batter.

5) Spoon your batter into the unbleached baking cups, and place cups in a Pyrex pan. A typical batch yields 6 muffins. *I like to double my recipe and make 12 muffins at a time.*

6) Place Pyrex pan in the oven and cook muffins for 1 hour. Then transfer muffins to dehydrator tray and dehydrate for an additional 4-8 hours at 117 degrees. *The longer you dehydrate the muffins, the firmer they will be (freezing also firms muffins).*

7) When muffins are done, line a Pyrex container with unbleached parchment paper and layer the muffins. I store muffins in the freezer. I do not recommend reheating muffins — they are very good right out of the freezer, and thaw in a matter of minutes at room temperature.

Cupcakes

Top these versatile muffins with raw frosting (*see "Raw Frostings" section*) and you have a wonderful, nutritious cupcake. Peppermint frosting is especially nice with this muffin. *I like to pull out frosting and top my muffins as a quick and easy treat!*

"Mock" Oatmeal Muffins

These muffins have a wonderful aroma and taste great!

Health Benefits

This delicious treat contains an abundance of nutrients. It is a great source of protein as well as vitamins A, B, D, E, and K, plus calcium, iron, potassium, phosphorous, zinc, manganese, magnesium, and omega-3 and omega-6 fatty acids. The carob used in this recipe is up to 8 percent protein, and contains vitamins A, B, B2, B3, and D. It is also high in calcium, phosphorus, potassium, and magnesium, and contains some iron and manganese.

What you will need: *I suggest doubling this recipe*

1 cup of soaked organic sunflower seeds. Sunflower seeds will expand.

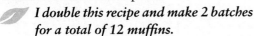 *I double this recipe and make 2 batches for a total of 12 muffins.*
I find if I soak 1 1/4 cups of sunflower seeds I generally will get 2 cups

3 Tb. of organic raw agave

1/2 Tb. of Frontier organic vanilla flavoring
Please make sure to buy glycerin-based vanilla, not alcohol-based!

1/2 Tb. of raw carob powder

1/2 tsp. of organic cinnamon

1/8 tsp. of organic cloves

1/3 cup of purified water

Unbleached baking cups
I use Beyond Gourmet or If You Care brands, found in health food stores.

Large Glass Pyrex pan (9 x 13 in.)

Large-bowl food Processor

Steps:

1) Soak sunflower seeds for a minimum of 8 hours or overnight. Rinse well (*3 to 4 times*) and drain.

2) Preheat oven to 250 degrees.

3) Place all ingredients in the food processor: sunflower seeds, agave, vanilla, carob, cinnamon, cloves and water.

4) Blend for 2 to 3 minutes. Pause 2-3 times using a spoon to scrape any loose ingredients from the sides of the bowl and under the blade. Blend until you have a relatively smooth batter.

5) Spoon your batter into the unbleached baking cups and place baking cups in a Pyrex Pan. A typical batch yields 6 muffins. *I like to double my recipe and make 12 muffins at a time.*

6) Place Pyrex pan in the oven and cook muffins for 1 hour. Then transfer muffins to dehydrator tray and dehydrate for an additional 4-8 hours at 117 degrees. *The longer you dehydrate the muffins, the firmer they will be (freezing also firms muffins).*

7) When muffins are done, line a Pyrex container with unbleached parchment paper and layer muffins. I store muffins in the freezer. I do not recommend reheating muffins—they are very good right out of the freezer. They thaw in a matter of minutes at room temperature.

Cupcakes:

 This flavorful muffin is best topped with vanilla frosting (*see "Raw Frostings" section*), which really compliments the spice in this recipe. *I will often make raw frostings and keep them in the freezer. I like to pull out frosting and top my muffins as a quick and easy treat!*

Brownies

These brownies are sinfully delicious!

Health Benefits

It is amazing to think something that tastes this good could be such a great source of protein as well as vitamins A, B, D, E, and K. Mother Necessity Brownies contain calcium, iron, potassium, phosphorous, zinc, manganese, magnesium, and omega-3 and omega-6 fatty acids. The chocolate used in this recipe contributes a significant amount of magnesium, and is a rich source of flavonoids and antioxidants.

What you will need: *I suggest doubling this recipe*

1 cup of soaked organic sunflower seeds. Sunflower seeds will expand.

 I suggest doubling this recipe and making two batches for a total of 12 brownies.
I find if I soak 1 1/4 cups of sunflower seeds, I generally will get 2 cups.

3 Tb. of organic raw agave

1/4 cup of purified water

4 Tb. of Frontier organic vanilla flavoring.

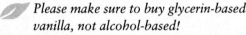 *Please make sure to buy glycerin-based vanilla, not alcohol-based!*

3 Tb. of organic, unsweetened chocolate powder or raw organic chocolate powder.

 I suggest using organic raw chocolate powder

1/2 tsp. of melted organic coconut oil.

 Place coconut oil in a glass Pyrex bowl and melt in the oven for 5 minutes at 350 degrees

Unbleached baking cups

 I use Beyond Gourmet or If You Care brands, found in health food stores.

Large Glass Pyrex Pan (9 x13 in.)

Large-bowl food processor

Steps:

1) Soak sunflower seeds for a minimum of 8 hours or overnight. Rinse well (*3 to 4 times*) and drain.

2) Preheat oven to 250 degrees.

3) Place all ingredients in the food processor: sunflower seeds, agave, vanilla, chocolate powder, coconut oil and water.

4) Blend for 2 to 3 minutes. Pause 2-3 times using a spoon to scrape any loose ingredients from the sides of the bowl and under the blade. Blend until you have a relatively smooth batter.

5) Spoon your batter into the unbleached baking cups and place baking cups in a Pyrex pan. A typical batch yields 6 brownies. *I like to double my recipe, and make 12 brownies at a time.*

6) Place Pyrex pan in the oven and cook brownies for 1 hour. Then transfer brownies to dehydrator tray and dehydrate for an additional 4-8 hours at 117 degrees. *The longer you dehydrate the brownies, the firmer they will be (freezing also firms brownies).*

7) When brownies are done, line a Pyrex container with unbleached parchment paper and layer the brownies. I store my brownies in the freezer. I do not recommend reheating brownies — they are very good right out of the freezer. They thaw in a matter of minutes at room temperature.

Optional - 1/8 tsp of organic peppermint flavor—gives this brownie a different twist!

I encourage everyone to use this recipe as a base and modify ingredients based on individual taste buds (more or less chocolate, vanilla, agave, etc.)

Raw Frostings

The following frostings are a wonderful way to enjoy sweets, without consuming refined sugars. All frostings are compatible with muffins (see muffin/cupcake section) to make a customized cupcake based on your desired taste and nutritional needs.

Raw frostings are a rich source of protein, vitamins, minerals, and essential fatty acids. All frostings can be made ahead of time and kept in the freezer to be used at your convenience. *I suggest freezing in a glass Pyrex container.*

When making raw frostings I recommend blending in a handheld blender such as Braun. The Cuisinart Mini Prep food processor does not effectively grind the small amount of nuts and seeds called for in this recipe and leaves the frosting very coarse. The Braun hand-held on the other hand completely pulverizes these ingredients and gives this frosting a nice smooth texture.

If you do not have a Braun handheld I recommend doubling this recipe and using the Cuisinart Mini Food Prep.

Raw Frostings

Frosting consistency will be thick and creamy

If you would like a thinner frosting you can add an additional 1 tsp. of purified water. I personally like the consistency of this frosting when frozen or chilled. I suggest placing frosting in the freezer for a minimum of one hour before using.

Chocolate Frosting

Place all ingredients in a handheld blender and blend until smooth

1/4 cup of soaked organic almonds

2 Tb. of purified water

2 Tb. of organic raw agave

2 Tb. of Frontier organic vanilla flavoring
  Please make sure to buy glycerin-based vanilla, not alcohol-based!

2 Tb. of unsweetened organic chocolate powder or organic raw chocolate powder
  I suggest using organic raw chocolate powder

Green Mint Frosting

Place all ingredients in a handheld blender and blend until smooth

1/4 cup of soaked organic almonds

1 ½ Tb. of purified water

2 Tb. of organic raw agave

2 Tb. of Frontier organic vanilla flavoring
  Please make sure to buy glycerin-based vanilla, not alcohol-based!

1 Tb. of raw carob powder

1/8 tsp. of organic peppermint flavoring
  Please make sure to buy glycerin-based peppermint, not alcohol-based!

1/2 tsp. of Mother Necessity Essential Greens or equivalent green powder

Raw Frostings

Frosting consistency will be thick and creamy

If you would like a thinner frosting you can add an additional 1 tsp. of purified water. I personally like the consistency of this frosting when frozen or chilled. I suggest placing frosting in the freezer for a minimum of one hour before using.

"Mock" Chocolate Frosting

made with carob

Place all ingredients in a handheld blender and blend until smooth

1/4 cup of soaked organic almonds

1 Tb. + 1 tsp. of purified water

2 Tb. of organic raw agave

2 Tb. of Frontier organic vanilla flavoring
 *Please make sure to buy glycerin-based vanilla, not alcohol-based!*

1 Tb. of raw carob powder

Vanilla Frosting

very nice with pumpkin muffins and oatmeal muffins

Place all ingredients in a handheld blender and blend until smooth

1/4 cup of soaked organic almonds

1 Tb. + 1 tsp. of purified water

2 Tb. of organic raw agave

2 tsp. of Frontier organic vanilla flavoring
Please make sure to buy glycerin-based vanilla, not alcohol-based!

Flat Bread, Crackers, French Toast, "Mock" Waffles & Pancakes

Grains, in their whole state, are considered much healthier than flours. Unlike processed flours, whole grains are packed with vitamins and minerals that are good for the heart and immune system. Whole grains not only taste better than flours, but they are far more nutritious, and easier to digest. Whole grains are a wonderful way to incorporate vitamins, minerals, and fiber into a diet.

When utilizing whole grains, proper preparation is very important to ensure proper digestion. Grains contain phytic acid and/or enzyme inhibitors. Enzyme inhibitors prevent enzyme action, while phytic acid inhibits mineral absorption. It is important to soak all grains prior to preparing recipes. This ensures that the body is able to metabolize and assimilate all nutrients.

In order to maintain healthy blood sugar levels, all of Mother Necessity grain recipes have been combined with healthy fats to slow the rate at which carbohydrates enter the bloodstream and influence blood sugar.

Similar to other Mother Necessity recipes, grain recipes are quick, easy, and versatile. You will find that flat breads can easily be transformed into crackers, waffles, and even French toast.

The grains used in the following recipe section are an excellent source of complex carbohydrates, and essential nutrients. They are "whole", gluten-free grains that are nutritionally superior to refined grains and flours.

Please Note: While the Cuisinart Mini Food Prep is effective at making these recipes, the Vitamix is a superior machine that will make multi-batches of flawless breads, waffles and pancakes everytime!

Millet Flat Bread

This grain makes wonderful-tasting flat bread.

Health Benefits

This bread is rich in magnesium, potassium, phosphorus, and B vitamins. Millet is a high in protein, and is considered to be a low-allergy grain. It is easy to digest and highly alkaline.

What you will need:

2/3 cup of organic soaked millet.

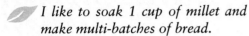 *I like to soak 1 cup of millet and make multi-batches of bread.*

3/4 cup of purified water

1 Tb. of organic unrefined coconut oil

1/2 tsp. of Celtic sea salt or crystal Himalayan salt

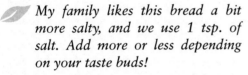 *My family likes this bread a bit more salty, and we use 1 tsp. of salt. Add more or less depending on your taste buds!*

Large Glass Pyrex pan (9 x 13 in.)

Cuisinart MiniPrep food processor or Vitamix.

For Thicker Bread:

1 cup of soaked, organic millet

1 cup of purified water

1 tsp. of Celtic sea salt or crystal Himalayan salt

Bake for 30 minutes

 Note: if bread is not cooking evenly please refer to page 25 "Flat breads unevenly cooked".

Steps:

1) Soak millet in a jar for a minimum of 8 hours or overnight. Rinse well (*3 to 4 times*) and drain.

2) Preheat oven to 350 degrees.

3) Grease pyrex glass pan with 1 Tb. of melted organic coconut oil. Make sure to spread evenly. *This recipe requires more oil as the grain has a tendency to dry out with heat.*

4) After soaking and rinsing grain, place 2/3 cup of grain in processor and grind for 1 minute or until fully ground.

5) Add remaining ingredients: water and salt. Grind for an additional 1 to 2 minutes. *If using a Vitamix, all ingredients can be combined and blended at the same time.*

6) Pour batter into glass Pyrex pan with coconut oil. *Always grind batter right before pouring into pan. Grain has a tendency to settle on the bottom when left to sit.*

7) Stir combined ingredients in the pan with a slow whisking motion to ensure that coconut oil, water, and grain are evenly distributed.

8) Bake at 350 degrees for 25 minutes.

9) Once cooled (*very important*), cut bread into strips the short way. Once strips are cut, take a spatula and gently work your way under the bread and peel up strips. One pan should yield 4 to 5 strips, or two rollups.

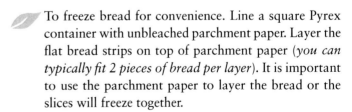 To freeze bread for convenience. Line a square Pyrex container with unbleached parchment paper. Layer the flat bread strips on top of parchment paper (*you can typically fit 2 pieces of bread per layer*). It is important to use the parchment paper to layer the bread or the slices will freeze together.

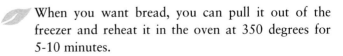 When you want bread, you can pull it out of the freezer and reheat it in the oven at 350 degrees for 5-10 minutes.

Do not pick up bread before it cools—it could break. It becomes much firmer once cooled.

Quinoa Flat Bread

Quinoa is a nutritious grain that typically has a strong taste — until now! This savory bread has a wonderful texture and a nice light buttery taste.

Health Benefits

This delicious bread is rich in amino acids, and very high in calcium and magnesium. It is a gluten-free grain that contains manganese, iron, phosphorous, zinc, and vitamins B2 and E, as well as dietary fiber.

What you will need:

3/4 cup of organic soaked quinoa.

 I like to soak 1 cup of quinoa and make multiple batches of bread.

3/4 cup of purified water

1 tsp. of organic ghee

1/2 tsp. of Celtic sea salt or crystal Himalayan salt

 My family likes this bread a bit more salty, and we use 1 tsp. of salt. Add more or less depending on your taste buds!

Large Glass Pyrex Pan (9 x 13 in.)

Cuisinart Mini-Prep food processor or Vitamix.

For Thicker Bread:

1 cup of soaked, organic quinoa

1 cup of purified water

1 tsp. of Celtic sea salt or crystal Himalayan salt

Bake for 48 minutes

 Note: *if bread is not cooking evenly please refer to page 25 "Flat breads unevenly cooked".*

Steps:

1) Soak quinoa in a jar for a minimum of 8 hours or overnight. Rinse well (*3 to 4 times*) and drain.

2) Preheat oven to 350 degrees.

3) Grease pyrex glass pan with 1 tsp. of melted organic ghee. Make sure to spread evenly.

4) After soaking and rinsing grain, place 3/4 cup of grain in processor and grind for 1 minute or until fully ground.

5) Add remaining ingredients: water and salt and grind for an additional 1 to 2 minutes. *If using a Vitamix, all ingredients can be combined and blended at the same time.*

6) Pour batter into glass Pyrex pan with ghee. *Always grind batter right before pouring into pan. Grain has a tendency to settle on the bottom when left to sit.*

7) Stir combined ingredients in the pan with a slow whisking motion to ensure that ghee, water, and grain are evenly distributed.

8) Bake at 350 degrees for 35 minutes.

9) Once cooled (*very important*), cut bread into strips the short way. Once strips are cut, take a spatula and gently work your way under the bread and peel up strips. One pan should yield 4 to 5 strips, or two rollups.

 To freeze bread for convenience. Line a square Pyrex container with unbleached parchment paper. Layer the flat bread strips on top of parchment paper (*you can typically fit 2 pieces of bread per layer*). It is important to use the parchment paper to layer the bread or the slices will freeze together.

 When you want bread, you can pull it out of the freezer and reheat it in the oven at 350 degrees for 5-10 minutes.

Do not pick up bread before it cools—it could break. It becomes much firmer once cooled.

Brown Rice Flat Bread

This delicious bread just melts in your mouth!

Health Benefits

Brown rice is a quality source of vitamins B1, B2, B3, and B6 as well as manganese, iron, selenium, magnesium, phosphorous, and trace minerals. Brown rice contains protein and amino acids and is recommended as a low-allergy alternative grain.

What you will need:

3/4 cup of soaked, whole-grain organic brown rice

 I personally feel short-grain rice makes better tasting bread

3/4 cup of purified water

1/2 Tb. of organic unrefined coconut oil

1/2 tsp. of Celtic sea salt or crystal Himalayan salt

 My family likes this bread a bit more salty, and we use 1 tsp. of salt. Add more or less depending on your taste buds!

Large Glass Pyrex Pan (9 x 13 in.)

Cuisinart Mini Prep food processor or Vitamix.

For Thicker Bread:

1 cup of soaked, organic short grain brown rice

3/4 cup of purified water

1 tsp. of Celtic sea salt or crystal Himalayan salt

Bake for 40 minutes

 Note: *if bread is not cooking evenly please refer to page 25 "Flat breads unevenly cooked".*

Steps:

1) Soak brown rice in a jar for a minimum of 8 hours or overnight. Rinse well (3-4 times) and drain.

2) Preheat oven to 350 degrees.

3) Grease pyrex glass pan with 1/2 Tb. of melted organic coconut. Make sure to spread evenly.

4) After soaking and rinsing grain, place 3/4 cup of grain in processor and grind for 1 minute or until fully ground.

5) Add remaining ingredients: water and salt and grind for an additional 1 to 2 minutes. *If using a Vitamix, all ingredients can be combined and blended at the same time.*

6) Pour batter into glass Pyrex pan with coconut oil. *Always grind batter right before pouring into pan. Grain has a tendency to settle on the bottom when left to sit—especially brown rice!*

7) Stir combined ingredients in the pan with a fork. Do not be concerned if grain and water separate, similar to sand in water. Use a slow whisking motion to ensure that coconut oil, water, and grain are evenly distributed.

8) Bake at 350 degrees for 35 minutes.

9) Once cooled (very important), cut bread into strips the short way. Once strips are cut, take a spatula and gently work your way under the bread and peel up strips. One pan should yield 4 to 5 strips, or two rollups.

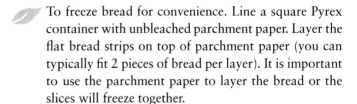 To freeze bread for convenience. Line a square Pyrex container with unbleached parchment paper. Layer the flat bread strips on top of parchment paper (you can typically fit 2 pieces of bread per layer). It is important to use the parchment paper to layer the bread or the slices will freeze together.

 When you want bread, you can pull it out of the freezer and reheat it in the oven at 350 degrees for 5-10 minutes. *Do not pick up bread before it cools—it could break.*

Millet Flat Bread Crackers

These crackers taste great and are a versatile, fun snack!

Health Benefits
This cracker is rich in magnesium, potassium, phosphorus, and B vitamins. Millet is high in protein, and is considered to be a low-allergy grain. The protein content of millet is generally superior to wheat, corn, and rice. It is a good source of fiber and offers protection against heart disease, cancer, and diabetes.

What you will need:

4 strips (*or 1 tray*) of freshly made or frozen millet flat bread.

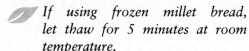 *If using frozen millet bread, let thaw for 5 minutes at room temperature.*

1/2 Tb. of organic unrefined coconut oil

1/4 tsp. of Celtic sea salt or crystal Himalayan salt

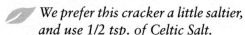 *We prefer this cracker a little saltier, and use 1/2 tsp. of Celtic Salt.*

Large Glass Pyrex Pan (9 x 13 in.)

Steps:

1) Preheat oven to 350 degrees.

2) Place 1/2 Tb. of coconut oil in glass pan and place in the oven until melted.

3) Cut millet flat bread into small squares or any fun shapes. *I will sometimes use small cookie cutters*

4) Place millet flat bread pieces in Pyrex pan with melted coconut oil.

5) Sprinkle 1/2 tsp. of salt over bread pieces.

6) Stir combined ingredients to evenly distribute oil and salt.

7) Bake for 15 min. at 350 degrees or until crackers are at the desired consistency. *Add an additional 5 min. cooking time for bread that has been previously frozen 20 min. total cooking time.*

8) Remove from oven. Let cool and enjoy!

Crackers can be enjoyed on salads or topped with fresh veggies, avocado, and even tomato sauce.

Quinoa Flat Bread Crackers

These crackers are my version of Frito Lay Corn Chips.

Health Benefits

This cracker is rich in amino acids and very high in calcium and magnesium. Quinoa is a gluten-free grain that contains manganese, iron, phosphorous, zinc, and vitamins B2 and E as well as dietary fiber. Quinoa is easy to digest and contains lysine, which is a potent antiviral agent.

What you will need:

4 strips (*or 1 tray*) of freshly made or frozen quinoa flat bread.

 If using frozen quinoa bread, let thaw for 5 minutes at room temperature.

1/2 Tb. ghee

1/4 tsp. of Celtic sea salt or crystal Himalayan salt

 We prefer this cracker a little saltier, and use 1/2 tsp. of Celtic Salt.

Large Glass Pyrex Pan (9 x 13 in.)

Steps:

1) Preheat oven to 350 degrees.

2) Place 1/2 Tb. of ghee in glass pan and place in the oven until melted.

3) Cut quinoa flat bread into small squares or any fun shapes. *I will sometimes use small cookie cutters.*

4) Place quinoa flat bread pieces in Pyrex pan with melted ghee.

5) Sprinkle salt over bread pieces.

6) Stir combined ingredients to evenly distribute oil and salt.

7) Bake for 15 min. at 350 degrees or until crackers are at the desired consistency. *Add an additional 5 min. cooking time for bread that has been previously frozen. 20 min. total cooking time.*

8) Remove from oven. Let cool and enjoy!

Crackers can be enjoyed on salads or topped with fresh veggies, avocado, and even tomato sauce.

Brown Rice Flat Bread Crackers

This cracker is a family favorite in my house.

Health Benefits
These crackers are not only delicious but they are also a quality source of vitamins B1, B2, B3, and B6 as well as manganese, iron, selenium, magnesium, phosphorous, and trace minerals. Brown rice is a good source of protein, amino acids, and gamma-oryzanol, an extract of rice bran oil that has been used to treat digestive, menopausal, and cholesterol-related problems.

What you will need:

4 strips (*or 1 tray*) of freshly made or frozen brown rice flat bread.

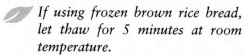 *If using frozen brown rice bread, let thaw for 5 minutes at room temperature.*

1/2 Tb. of organic unrefined coconut oil

1/4 tsp. of Celtic sea salt or crystal Himalayan salt

We prefer this cracker a little saltier, and use 1/2 tsp. of Celtic Salt.

Large Glass Pyrex Pan (9 x 13 in.)

Steps:

1) Preheat oven to 350 degrees.

2) Place 1/2 Tb. of coconut oil in glass pan and place in the oven until melted.

3) Cut brown rice flat bread into small squares or any fun shapes. *I will sometimes use small cookie cutters*

4) Place brown rice flat bread pieces in glass Pyrex pan with melted coconut oil.

5) Sprinkle salt over bread pieces.

6) Stir combined ingredients to evenly distribute oil and salt.

7) Bake for 15 min. at 350 degrees or until crackers are at the desired consistency. *Add an additional 5 min. cooking time for bread that has been previously frozen—20 min. total cooking time.*

8) Remove from oven. Let cool and enjoy!

Crackers can be enjoyed on salads or topped with fresh veggies, avocado, and even tomato sauce.

Almond Crackers

These crackers are my version of
Ritz Crackers.

Health Benefits

These crackers contain protein, fiber, potassium, magnesium, calcium, iron, zinc, folic acid, and vitamins B2, B3, and E. Almonds are very alkalizing and have been found to play an effective role in lowering cholesterol and reducing heart disease.

What you will need:

2 cups of soaked organic almonds. Almonds will expand.

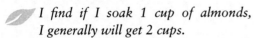 *I find if I soak 1 cup of almonds, I generally will get 2 cups.*

5 Tb. of purified water

2 Tb. of organic melted ghee.

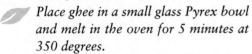 *Place ghee in a small glass Pyrex bowl and melt in the oven for 5 minutes at 350 degrees.*

3/4 tsp. of Celtic sea salt or crystal Himalayan salt.

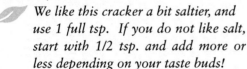 *We like this cracker a bit saltier, and use 1 full tsp. If you do not like salt, start with 1/2 tsp. and add more or less depending on your taste buds!*

Large-bowl food processor

Steps:

1) Soak almonds for a minimum of 8 hours or overnight. Rinse well (*3 to 4 times*) and drain. *If you would like to take the skin off the almonds, simply place almonds in a strainer and pour hot water over them. Skins should peel off—an additional rinse is suggested.*

2) Place well-rinsed almonds in a food processor and blend until coarse.

3) Add remaining ingredients: water, ghee, and salt.

4) Blend for 2 to 3 minutes or until smooth. Pause 3 to 4 times and take a spoon to scrape any loose ingredients from the sides of the bowl and below the blade. Blend until you have a relatively smooth paste (may still have some lumps), similar to cookie dough.

5) After processing, roll a spoonful of batter into your hands, press into a flat cracker (half dollar size), and place on dehydrator tray. *A much quicker approach to making crackers is to simply spread a thin layer of batter on the dehydrator tray. Then take a butter knife and lightly cut batter into small squares (a lot less time consuming then making circle-shaped crackers by hand).*

6) Dehydrate crackers at 117 degrees for 24 hours or until desired consistency is reached. The longer you dehydrate, the crunchier your crackers will be. Dehydrate based on your desired consistency.

I encourage everyone to use this recipe as a base and modify ingredients based on individual taste buds (more or less salt, ghee, etc.).

Cracker Topping Ideas

The following cracker topping ideas are versatile and can be used to top flat breads, crackers or sandwiches. Please use these recipes as a base. I encourage everyone to add their personal taste and flair to customize these recipes.

When making dips I suggest using a handheld blender such as Braun. The Cuisinart Mini Prep food processor does not effectively grind these recipes, which results in a coarsely chopped dip—While the Braun handheld will produce a nice smooth texture

Basic Avocado Dip

1 ripe avocado

Optional 1/2 tsp. of freshly squeezed organic lime

Mash ingredients with a fork, potato masher or in handheld blender until smooth.

Basic Almond and Spinach Dip

1/2 cup of organic soaked almonds

1 Tb. of melted organic ghee

1 tsp. of vegetable glycerin

3 Tb. of purified water

1/4 tsp. of Celtic sea salt or crystal Himalayan salt

2 Tb. of organic spinach, steamed or cooked until warm (*approx. 5 minutes*)

Combine all ingredients EXCEPT spinach in Braun handheld blender or equivalent small size blender. Blend until you have a smooth dip.

Add spinach and process for an additional 60 seconds (*until spinach is coarsely combined with dip*)

Serve at room temperature or warm in the oven at 250 degrees for 10 minutes.

Basic Almond Butter

1/4 cup of organic soaked almonds

1 tsp. of melted organic ghee

2 Tb. of raw organic agave

2 Tb. of purified water

1/2 tsp. of Celtic sea salt or crystal Himalayan salt

Combine all ingredients in Braun handheld blender or equivalent small size blender. Blend until you have a smooth dip.

Basic Pumpkin Seed Butter

1/4 cup of organic soaked pumpkin seeds

1/4 cup of organic peeled carrots (*approx. 1/2 a carrot*)

2 Tb. of raw organic agave

1/2 Tb. of Frontier organic vanilla flavoring.
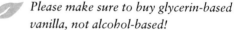 *Please make sure to buy glycerin-based vanilla, not alcohol-based!*

1/4 tsp. of Celtic sea salt or crystal Himalayan salt

Optional – 1/4 tsp. of melted organic coconut oil (gives this dip a sweet nutty flavor)

Place carrots in handheld blender and shred.

Combine remaining ingredients and blend until you have a smooth dip.

"Mock" Peanut Butter made with Sunflower Seeds

1/2 cup of organic soaked sunflower seeds

2 Tb. of raw organic agave

1 Tb. of organic vanilla flavoring.
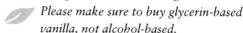 *Please make sure to buy glycerin-based vanilla, not alcohol-based.*

1/4 tsp. of Celtic sea salt or crystal Himalayan salt

1 tsp. of raw carob powder

Combine all ingredients in handheld blender and blend until you have a smooth dip.

Optional – *I like to add 1 Tsp. of Mother Necessity Essential Greens to this recipe. It tastes great and adds wonderful nutritional benefits.*

Millet French Toast

This is a wonderful healthy version of French toast.

Health Benefits
Millet French toast is rich in protein magnesium, potassium, phosphorus, and B vitamins. It is also good source of fiber, and offers protection against heart disease, cancer, and diabetes. The high protein content of millet is generally superior to wheat, corn, and rice.

What you will need:

1 cup of organic soaked millet

3/4 cup of purified water

1 Tb. of organic agave

1 Tb. of organic unrefined coconut oil – *to grease glass pan*

Additional – 1 tsp. of melted organic unrefined coconut oil – to mix in batter

1/4 tsp. of Celtic sea salt

1 tsp. of organic cinnamon

1 small scoop of stevia (*scooper is in stevia bottle*), or to taste

 Stevia is very sweet-make sure to add only a small amount at a time (barely a pinch)

Large Glass Pyrex Pan (9 x 13 in.)

Cuisinart Mini Prep food processor or Vita-Mix

Steps:

1) Soak millet in a jar for a minimum of 8 hrs. or overnight. Rinse well (*3 to 4 times*) and drain.

2) Preheat oven to 350 degrees.

3) Grease pyrex glass pan with 1 Tb. of melted organic coconut oil. Make sure to spread evenly. *This recipe requires more oil as the grain has a tendency to dry out with heat.*

4) After soaking and rinsing grain, place 1 cup of grain in processor and grind for 1 minute or until fully ground.

5) Add remaining ingredients to food processor: water, salt, cinnamon, stevia, agave and additional 1 tsp. of melted coconut oil. Grind for 1 to 2 minutes. *If using a Vitamix all ingredients can be combined and blended at the same time.*

6) Pour batter into glass Pyrex pan with coconut oil. *Always grind batter right before pouring into pan. Grain has a tendency to settle on the bottom when left to sit.*

7) Stir combined batter ingredients in the pan with a slow whisking motion to ensure that grain and liquid are evenly distributed.

8) Place Pyrex pan in the oven and bake for 32 minutes at 350 degrees.

9) After removing French toast from oven, let cool. Once cooled (*very important or French toast will break*) cut French toast into sticks, squares, or even into fun shapes using stainless steel cookie cutters.

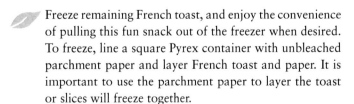 Freeze remaining French toast, and enjoy the convenience of pulling this fun snack out of the freezer when desired. To freeze, line a square Pyrex container with unbleached parchment paper and layer French toast and paper. It is important to use the parchment paper to layer the toast or slices will freeze together.

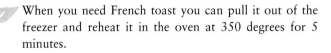 When you need French toast you can pull it out of the freezer and reheat it in the oven at 350 degrees for 5 minutes.

French toast topping can be achieved by taking 1 Tb. of organic agave and mixing with ¼ tsp. organic cinnamon

Quinoa Pancakes

This is a great alternative to traditional pancakes and contains an array of vitamins and minerals.

Health Benefits
These pancakes are rich in amino acids, and very high in calcium and magnesium. Quinoa is a gluten-free grain that contains manganese, iron, phosphorous, zinc, and vitamins B2 and E, as well as dietary fiber and protein.

What you will need:

1 cup of organic soaked quinoa

1 cup of purified water

1 tsp. of organic ghee

1/2 tsp. of Celtic sea salt

Large Glass Pyrex Pan (9 × 13 in.)

Cuisinart Mini Prep food processor or Vita-Mix

Topping Option:

2 Tb. of Vegetable glycerin
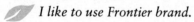 *I like to use Frontier brand.*

1 tsp. of Frontier organic vanilla flavoring.
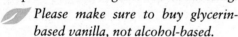 *Please make sure to buy glycerin-based vanilla, not alcohol-based.*

1/8 tsp. of organic cinnamon

Pinch of organic cloves

Steps:

1) Soak quinoa in a jar for a min. of 8 hrs. or overnight. Rinse well (*3 to 4 times*) and drain.

2) Preheat oven to 350 degrees.

3) Grease pyrex glass pan with 1 tsp. of melted organic ghee. Spread evenly.

4) After soaking and rinsing grain, place 1 cup of grain in processor and grind for 1 minute or until fully ground.

5) Add remaining ingredients: water, and salt. Grind for an additional 1 to 2 minutes. *If using a Vitamix all ingredients can be combined and blended at the same time).*

6) Pour batter into glass Pyrex pan with ghee. *Always grind batter right before pouring into pan. Grain has a tendency to settle on the bottom when left to sit.*

7) Bake at 350 degrees for 48 minutes.

8) Combine pancake topping ingredients in a small bowl. Mix thoroughly.

9) After removing pancakes from oven, let them sit and cool (*very important or they will break*), then use a stainless steel circular cookie cutter, or round glass rim to cut out perfectly round silver dollar pancakes. If you feel creative, you can use alternative cookie cutters to make other fun shapes.

After cutting out your pancakes top with glycerin topping, ghee and/ or cinnamon.

Leftover pancakes can be frozen and used at a later date. I enjoy the convenience of pulling this fun snack out of the freezer when needed. To freeze, line a square Pyrex container with unbleached parchment paper and layer pancakes and paper. It is important to use the parchment paper to layer pancakes or they will freeze together.

Vegetable Glycerin makes a great topping—it is tasty on any breads, pancakes, and even crackers.

Brown Rice "Mock" Waffles

This waffle is one of my son's longtime favorites.

Health Benefits

Brown rice is a quality source of protein and amino acids. It contains vitamins B1, B2, B3, and B6; as well as manganese, iron, selenium, magnesium, phosphorous, and trace minerals. Brown rice is recommended as a low-allergy grain and is by far the most nutritional rice form available.

What you will need:

1 cup of soaked organic short–grain brown rice

3/4 cup of purified water

1/2 Tb. of organic unrefined coconut oil

1/4 tsp. of Celtic sea salt

2 Tb. of organic agave

2 Tb. of Frontier organic vanilla flavoring.

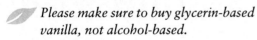 *Please make sure to buy glycerin-based vanilla, not alcohol-based.*

1 small scoop of stevia (*scooper is in bottle*), or to taste

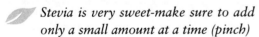 *Stevia is very sweet-make sure to add only a small amount at a time (pinch)*

Large Glass Pyrex Pan (9 x 13 in.)

Cuisinart Mini Prep food processor or Vita-Mix

Steps:

1) Soak brown rice for a min. of 8 hrs. or overnight. Rinse well (*3 to 4 times*) and drain.

2) Preheat oven to 350 degrees.

3) Grease pyrex glass pan with 1/2 Tb. of melted organic coconut oil. Spread evenly.

4) After soaking and rinsing grain, place 1 cup of grain in processor and grind for 1 minute or until fully ground.

5) Add remaining ingredients: water, salt, agave, vanilla and stevia. Grind for an additional 1 to 2 minutes. *If using a Vitamix, all ingredients can be combined and blended at the same time.*

6) Pour batter into glass Pyrex pan with coconut oil. *Always grind batter right before pouring into pan. Grain has a tendency to settle on the bottom when left to sit—especially brown rice!*

7) Stir combined ingredients in the pan. Do not be concerned if grain and water separate, similar to sand in water. Use a slow whisking motion to ensure that grain and liquid are evenly distributed.

8) Bake at 350 degrees for 35 minutes.

9) After removing waffles from oven, let them sit and cool (very important). Then use a stainless steel circular cookie cutter, or round glass rim, to cut out perfectly round waffles. You can then take a fork or a fun-shape cookie cutter and make indentations on top of waffles, to simulate the "waffle" look.

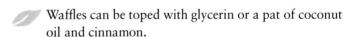 Waffles can be toped with glycerin or a pat of coconut oil and cinnamon.

Leftover waffles can be frozen and used at a later date. I enjoy the convenience of pulling this fun snack out of the freezer when needed. To freeze, line a square Pyrex container with unbleached parchment paper and layer waffles and paper. It is important to use the parchment paper to layer waffles or they will freeze together.

notes

Entrées

The following entrées are a great way to indulge in your favorite foods—the healthy way. All recipes are quick, easy, and interchangeable.

As important as it was for my family to remove common allergens and "reactive" food sources from our diets, it was equally important to develop foods that looked and tasted like the foods we had been accustomed to eating. I wanted healthy living to be a lifestyle for my family, not a punishment.

Hence I recreated all of my family's favorite foods into healthy foods. All of the recipes in this section are packed full of nutrition and taste. They are made without the use of refined flours, sugars and other nutritionally void ingredients.

Mother Necessity entrées are rich in protein, amino acids, fiber and vitamins and minerals. All recipes use minimal ingredients to ensure proper digestion and assimilation of nutrients.

I encourage everyone to use these recipes as base and incorporate as many healthy variations as possible. The more nutritional options we incorporate into our diets, the more energy and vitality we will have.

Pizza Pie

It is hard to believe that this pizza is Gluten Free/Casein Free.
This is an all-time favorite in our family!

Health Benefits
**Unlike traditional pizza, Mother Necessity
pizza contains no gluten or casein and is rich
in protein, fiber, calcium, magnesium, potassium,
phosphorus, iron, zinc, folic acid, beta-carotene,
vitamin C, and B vitamins.**

What you will need for pizza crust:

2/3 cup of organic soaked millet

2/3 cup of purified water

1/2 Tb. of organic unrefined coconut oil

1/2 tsp. of Celtic sea salt or crystal
Himalayan salt

Round Glass Pyrex pan

Cuisinart Mini-Prep food processor
or Vita-Mix

What you will need for "mock" cheese:

1 1/2 cup of soaked organic almonds

2 Tb. of organic melted ghee

4 Tb. of purified water

1/2 tsp. of Celtic sea salt or crystal
Himalayan salt

Mini Prep food processor or hand-held
blender

What you will need for sauce:

1 glass jar of organic tomato paste.
*Do not use food items that
come in a metal can.*

1 cup organic diced tomato
(approx 1 large tomato)

2 tsp. of organic basil

Optional – 1/2 tsp. of fresh organic garlic

1/2 tsp. of organic thyme

1/4 tsp. of organic rosemary

2 tsp. of glycerin.
I like to use Frontier brand.

1/2 tsp. of Celtic sea salt or crystal
Himalayan salt

Steps for crust:

1) Soak millet in a jar for a minimum of 8 hours or overnight. Rinse well (*3 to 4 times*) and drain.

2) Preheat oven to 350 degrees.

3) Grease pyrex glass pan with 1/2 Tb. of melted organic coconut oil. Spread evenly.

4) After soaking and rinsing grain, place millet in mini food processor and grind for 1 minute or until fully ground.

5) Add remaining ingredients: water and salt. Grind for an additional 1 to 2 minutes. *If using a Vitamix, all ingredients can be combined and blended at the same time.*

6) Pour batter into glass Pyrex pan with coconut oil. *Always grind batter right before pouring into pan. Grain has a tendency to settle on the bottom when left to sit.*

7) Stir combined ingredients in the pan with a slow whisking motion to ensure that coconut oil, water, and grain are evenly distributed.

8) Bake crust at 350 degrees for 35 minutes.

Steps for "Mock" cheese:

1) Combine all ingredients listed under cheese in a handheld blender or mini food processor.

2) Blend for 2 to 3 minutes. I recommend stopping two or three times and using a spoon to scrape any loose ingredients from the sides of the bowl and under the blade.

3) Blend until all ingredients are relatively smooth and well blended.

Steps for sauce:

1) Combine all of the sauce ingredients listed under "sauce" in a Pyrex stovetop pan. *Always make sure cookware is stovetop-compatible.*

2) Turn burner on medium heat and cook sauce for five minutes.

3) Reduce heat and let sauce simmer for an additional 10 minutes, stirring frequently.

4) After 15 minutes of cooking, sauce is ready to use.

 You can continue to cook sauce on the lowest setting, or turn burner off and let sauce sit on un-lit burner until crust is ready.

Steps for pizza:

1) Take baked pizza crust out of the oven. Top with tomato sauce and "Mock" cheese. Add additional toppings such as steamed spinach or other vegetables.

 Pizza can be enjoyed immediately after adding toppings or warmed in oven at 250 degrees for 10 minutes and served.

I encourage everyone to use this recipe as a base and modify ingredients based on individual taste buds. More or less tomatoes, spices, oil, etc.

Lasagna

This dish is just as delicious, if not more delicious, as traditional lasagna which contains gluten and casein.

Health Benefits
Not only does this lasagna taste amazing, it is also packed with nutrition and is rich in protein, fiber, calcium, magnesium, potassium, phosphorus, iron, zinc, folic acid, beta-carotene, vitamin C, and B vitamins.

What you will need for noodles:

9 strips of millet flat bread- equivalent to approx. 2 trays of millet flat bread (*see breads*).

Bread can be fresh or frozen.
When using frozen bread, let sit at room temperature until thawed (approx 5-10 minutes)

Medium Glass Pyrex Pan (8 × 8 in.)

What you will need for ricotta cheese:

1 cup of soaked organic almonds

2 Tb. of melted ghee

1/2 cup of purified water

2 tsp. of vegetable glycerin

1 tsp. of organic basil

1 tsp. of Celtic sea salt or crystal Himalayan salt

Large Bowl food processor

What you will need for sauce:

1 glass jar of organic tomato paste.
Do not use food items that come in a metal can.

1 cup organic diced tomato (approx 1 large tomato)

2 tsp. of organic basil

Optional – 1/2 tsp. of fresh organic garlic

1/2 tsp. of organic thyme

1/4 tsp. of organic rosemary

1 tsp. of vegetable glycerin.
I like to use Frontier brand.

1/2 tsp. of Celtic sea salt or crystal Himalayan salt.

Steps for sauce:

1) Combine all of the sauce ingredients listed under "sauce" in a Pyrex stovetop pan. *Always make sure cookware is stovetop-compatible.*

2) Turn burner on medium heat and cook sauce for five minutes.

3) After 15 minutes of cooking, sauce is ready to use.

You can continue to cook sauce on the lowest setting, or turn burner off and let sauce sit on un-lit burner until ready to use.

Steps for cheese:

1) Combine all of the ricotta cheese ingredients in a large bowl food processor.

2) Blend for 2 to 3 minutes.

3) Pause two or three times using a spoon to scrape any loose ingredients from the sides of the bowl and under the blade. Blend until all ingredients are relatively smooth and well blended.

Steps for lasagna:

1) Preheat oven to 250 degrees.

2) Spoon a small amount of sauce into an 8" x 8" Pyrex pan.

3) Place 3 strips of millet flat bread on top of sauce in Pyrex glass pan.

4) Top millet bread with "mock" ricotta cheese, (*optional*) steamed or thawed spinach, and sauce.

5) Continue layering. Place 3 more strips of bread on top of the sauce. Layer cheese, (*optional*) spinach, and sauce once again.

6) Place the last 3 millet strips on top of sauce. Top with sauce, cheese and optional spinach.

7) Place lasagna in preheated oven for 15 minutes or until desired temperature is reached. *When using freshly made millet bread, lasagna does not have to be heated. Please serve lasagna at your desired temperature.*

I encourage everyone to use this recipe as a base and modify ingredients based on individual taste buds. More or less sauce, cheese and flat bread.

Chicken Parmesan

This recipe proves that you can eat healthy without sacrificing taste!
Chicken Parmesan pairs very well with any Mother Necessity
Rice or Salad

Health Benefits
Chicken is a very good source of protein, niacin, selenium, and vitamin B6. It is also a good source of pantothenic acid and phosphorous. The addition of almonds and tomatoes adds additional protein, fiber, potassium, phosphorus, magnesium, calcium, iron, zinc, beta-carotene, folic acid, and vitamins C, B2, B3, and E.

What you will need for chicken:

3 boneless, skinless organic, free range chicken breasts. Free of hormones, antibiotics, and additives.

2 Tb. of organic ghee (*melted*)

1 ½ cup of frozen pre-made almond cookies. See "Cookie" section.

1/4 tsp. of Celtic sea salt or crystal Himalayan salt

Handheld or mini food processor

Large Pyrex Glass Pan (9 x 13 in.)

What you will need for cheese:

1/2 cup of soaked organic almonds

2 Tb. of melted ghee

4 Tb. of purified water

1/2 tsp. of Celtic sea salt or crystal Himalayan salt

Mini Prep food processor or hand-held blender

What you will need for sauce:

1 glass jar of organic tomato paste.
 Do not use food items that come in a metal can.

1 cup organic diced tomato (approx 1 large tomato)

2 tsp. of organic basil

Optional – 1/2 tsp. of fresh organic garlic

1/2 tsp. of organic thyme

1/4 tsp. of organic rosemary

2 tsp. of glycerin.
 *I like to use Frontier brand.*

1/2 tsp. of Celtic sea salt or crystal Himalayan salt

Steps for chicken:

1) Preheat oven to 250 degrees.

2) Combine almond cookies (right out of the freezer) and salt in handheld blender. Grind until you have the consistency of bread crumbs. *Make sure blender bowl is not wet — cookies will turn into a paste.*

3) Heat ghee to soften. Take a portion of the ghee to grease Pyrex pan. The rest is used to coat the chicken. You don't need to use a lot — just enough to make the cookie crumbs stick.

4) Once chicken is coated with ghee, sprinkle almond cookie crumbs on both sides of the chicken and place in glass Pyrex pan.

5) Cook at 250 degrees for 45 minutes.

6) When chicken is thoroughly cooked, spoon sauce and cheese on top of chicken and dinner is served.

Chicken Parmesan can be served immediately after placing sauce and cheese on top of chicken, or warmed in the oven at 250 degrees for 10 minutes.

Steps for sauce:

1) Combine all of the sauce ingredients in a Pyrex stovetop pan. *Always make sure cookware is stovetop-compatible.*

2) Turn burner on medium heat and cook sauce for five minutes.

3) Reduce heat and let sauce simmer for an additional 10 minutes, stirring frequently.

4) After 15 minutes of cooking, sauce is ready to use.

Sauce can remain on burner at lowest setting until chicken is ready (*continue to stir*)

Steps for cheese:

1) Combine cheese ingredients in food processor or handheld blender.

2) Blend for 2 to 3 minutes. Pause two or three times using a spoon to scrape any loose ingredients from the sides of the bowl and under the blade. Blend until all ingredients are relatively smooth and well blended.

I encourage everyone to use this recipe
as a base and modify ingredients based
on individual taste buds. More or less
sauce, cheese and breading.

Italian Meatballs

Right out of Boston's North End –
These meatballs are simply delicious!

Health Benefits
Beef is an excellent source of protein and vitamins B12 and B6. Beef also contains riboflavin, zinc, selenium, niacin, iron, and phosphorous. The addition of almonds and tomatoes adds additional protein, fiber, potassium, phosphorus, magnesium, calcium, iron, zinc, beta-carotene, folic acid, and vitamins C, B2, B3, and E to this wonderful dish.

What you will need for meatballs:

1 lb. of organic/free range grass-fed buffalo or beef. Free of hormones, antibiotics, and additives.

Optional – 1/4 cup of minced organic onion

1/2 Tb. of melted ghee

1 cup of pre-made almond cookies (out of the freezer)

1 tsp. of Celtic sea salt

1 tsp. of organic basil

Large Glass Pyrex Pan (9 x 13 in.)

Cuisinart Mini Prep food processor or hand-held blender

What you will need for sauce:

1 glass jar of organic tomato paste.
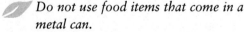
Do not use food items that come in a metal can.

1 cup organic diced tomato (approx 1 large tomato)

2 tsp. of organic basil

Optional – 1/2 tsp. of fresh organic garlic

1/2 tsp. of organic thyme

1/4 tsp. of organic rosemary

2 tsp. of vegetable glycerin.
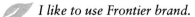
I like to use Frontier brand.

1/2 tsp. of Celtic sea salt

Steps for meatballs:

1) Preheat oven to 300 degrees.

2) Combine frozen cookies and salt in handheld blender or mini prep food processor. Grind until you have the consistency of bread crumbs. Make sure blender bowl is not wet — cookies will turn into a paste.

3) Combine cookies and salt with meat, melted ghee, and basil.

4) Knead all ingredients in a bowl until thoroughly mixed.

5) Roll meat into balls and place them in a glass Pyrex pan.

6) Cook at 300 degrees for 35 minutes.

7) Prepare Sauce while meatballs are cooking.

8) After 35 minutes of cooking remove meatballs from oven and place in red sauce and let simmer for 15 minutes or until thoroughly cooked.

Steps for sauce:

1) Combine all of the sauce ingredients in a glass Pyrex stovetop pan.

2) Always make sure cookware is stovetop-compatible.

3) Turn burner on lowest setting and cook sauce for fifteen minutes or until meatballs are ready to come out of the oven.

4) When meatballs are out of the oven increase stovetop heat (*medium heat*) and place meatballs in sauce.

5) Let meatballs simmer in red sauce for 15 minutes or until meatballs are thoroughly cooked.

Mother Necessity Veggie Meatballs

The following "veggie" meatball recipes were developed for my son, Dylan. In an effort to get my son to eat more vegetables I devised a plan to sneak in as many vegetables into his diet without him knowing - and believe it or not it worked!

I grind various vegetable combinations into his meats. He has no idea that he is eating them and they actually enhance the flavor and texture of the meatballs. It is a win, win situation.

Vegetables are a rich source of vitamins, minerals, carbohydrates, and protein. They pair very well with meats, which are a complete protein source, providing the body with all of the essential amino acids. When purchasing meats always choose organic, free-range sources that have not been subjected to hormones, antibiotics or agricultural chemicals.

I like to cook these meatballs in bulk and freeze them for quick dinners, lunches and snacks. They make a great replacement for cold cuts, which contain sodium nitrates. This common preservative can also be found in hot dogs and cured and smoked meats. It has been associated with various cancers and is believed to convert in the gut to cancer-promoting compounds called nitrosamines.

Everyday I take a different veggie meatball out of the freezer and heat it up for my son's luch. I then slice it thinly and put it between two pieces of Mother Necessity Flat Breads. My son loves his lunch, and I love that he is eating "whole" food nutrition.

Turkey Veggie Meatballs

This recipe makes a moist meatball that is very delicious!

Health Benefits
Turkey is a good source of protein, selenium, niacin, zinc, and vitamins B6 and B12. Broccoli adds wonderful nutritional benefits to this meatball as it is rich in calcium, magnesium, phosphorus, vitamin B, and beta-carotene. It is also high in vitamin C and folic acid, and demonstrates remarkable anticancer effects. Broccoli is an antioxidant, intestinal cleanser, antiviral agent, and an excellent source of fiber. The addition of collard greens and squash contribute additional vitamins, minerals, and dietary fiber to this dish.

What you will need:

1 lb. of organic, free-range turkey — free of antibiotics, hormones, and additives.

1 cup of frozen or fresh organic broccoli.

 I initially started with 1 cup of broccoli and have gradually increased to 2 cups.

1/4 cup of organic collard greens.

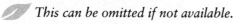 *This can be omitted if not available.*

1/2 cup of organic yellow squash

1 tsp. of Celtic sea salt

1/2 tsp. of organic oregano

Large Pyrex pan (9 x 13 in.)

Large-bowl food processor

Steps:

1) Preheat oven to 300 degrees.

2) Measure vegetables. To measure vegetables I fill a measuring cup with fresh or frozen broccoli. I then generally use 1/2 of a yellow squash and a half or a whole leaf of collard greens. *You can tear collard greens in small pieces and place in a measuring cup to measure approx. 1/4 cup.*

3) Place broccoli in the food processor and blend until coarse. Add collard greens and yellow squash and blend for 1 minute. Vegetables may still be mildly coarse — this is ok.

4) Add turkey, salt, and oregano to food processor. Blend until veggies and meat are thoroughly blended together.

5) Form meatballs or patties with the veggie/meat mix and place them in a glass Pyrex pan.

6) Cook at 300 degrees for 35 minutes or until thoroughly cooked.

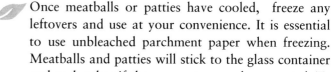 Once meatballs or patties have cooled, freeze any leftovers and use at your convenience. It is essential to use unbleached parchment paper when freezing. Meatballs and patties will stick to the glass container and each other if they are not properly separated. To freeze line a square Pyrex container with parchment paper and layer accordingly.

 To reheat, simply place patties or meatballs in a Pyrex pan and cook for 10 minutes at 300 degrees (*or until warm*). The end result is a balanced dinner, lunch, or snack!

Please use this recipe as a base. We have found that this recipe is a great way to add vegetables to everyone's diet. In our family we initially started out with the base recipe and have gradually increased our veggie-to-meat ratio. We now use double or triple the amount of vegetables. For us it is truly a veggie burger! Modify this recipe to suit your taste buds and nutritional needs.

Lamb Veggie Meatballs

These meatballs are so delectable that they will melt in your mouth.

Health Benefits

Lamb is an excellent source of vitamin B12 and protein. It is also contains selenium, niacin, zinc, phosphorous, and riboflavin. The asparagus used in this recipe provides potassium, vitamins A, B6, C, and K, as well as folic acid, riboflavin, and thiamin. In addition, asparagus contains dietary fiber, niacin, phosphorus, protein, and iron. Asparagus is a good source of glutathione, which is involved in detoxification and antioxidant mechanisms. The addition of zucchini and dandelion greens contribute additional vitamins, minerals, and dietary fiber to this dish.

What you will need:

1 lb. of organic, free-range lamb — free of antibiotics, hormones, and additives.

1 cup of fresh or frozen organic asparagus.

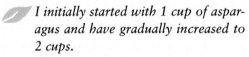 *I initially started with 1 cup of asparagus and have gradually increased to 2 cups.*

1/4 cup organic dandelion greens.

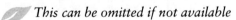 *This can be omitted if not available*

1/2 cup of organic zucchini

1 tsp. of Celtic sea salt

1/2 tsp. of organic thyme

Large Glass Pyrex Pan (9 x 13 in.)

Large-bowl food processor

Steps:

1) Preheat oven to 300 degrees.

2) Measure vegetables. To measure vegetables I break fresh or frozen asparagus in half and place in a measuring cup. I then generally use half of a zucchini and 2 dandelion green leaves. *You can tear greens into small pieces and place in a measuring cup to approx. 1/4 cup.*

3) Place asparagus in the food processor and blend until coarse. Add dandelion greens and zucchini and blend for 1 minute. Vegetables may still be mildly coarse—this is ok.

4) Add lamb, salt, and thyme to food processor. Blend until veggies and meat are thoroughly blended together.

5) Form meatballs or patties with veggie/meat mix and place in a Pyrex pan.

6) Cook at 300 degrees for 35 minutes or until thoroughly cooked.

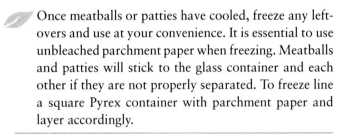 Once meatballs or patties have cooled, freeze any leftovers and use at your convenience. It is essential to use unbleached parchment paper when freezing. Meatballs and patties will stick to the glass container and each other if they are not properly separated. To freeze line a square Pyrex container with parchment paper and layer accordingly.

To reheat, simply place patties or meatballs in a Pyrex pan and cook for 10 minutes at 300 degrees (*or until warm*). The end result is a balanced dinner, lunch, or snack!

Please use this recipe as a base. We have found that this recipe is a great way to add vegetables to everyone's diet. In our family we initially started out with the base recipe and have gradually increased our veggie-to-meat ratio. We now use double or triple the amount of vegetables. For us it is truly a veggie burger! Modify this recipe to suit your taste buds and nutritional needs.

Veggie Ground Beef or Buffalo Meatballs

An all-time favorite! Both ground beef and buffalo work great in this recipe.

Health Benefits
Beef is an excellent source of protein and vitamins B12 and B6, which are two key vitamins for proper cellular function. Contrary to popular belief, lean red meat has no greater effect on blood cholesterol levels than equivalent amounts of lean chicken or turkey. Spinach is an excellent source of carotenes, folic acid, and vitamins C and K. It is also a very good source of manganese, magnesium, iron, and vitamins B1, B2, B6, and E. Like other chlorophyll and carotene containing vegetables, spinach is a strong protector against cancer. The addition of cucumber and kale also contribute additional vitamins, minerals, and dietary fiber to this dish

What you will need:

1 lb. of organic, free range grass-fed buffalo or ground beef — free of antibiotics, hormones, and additives.

1 cup of fresh or frozen organic spinach
I initially started with 1 cup of spinach and have gradually increased to 2 cups.

1/4 cup of organic kale.

This can be omitted if not available

1/2 cup of organic cucumber

1 tsp. of Celtic sea salt

1/2 tsp. of organic basil

Large Glass Pyrex Pan (9 x 13 in.)

Large-bowl food processor

Steps:

1) Preheat oven to 300 degrees.

2) Measure vegetables. To measure vegetables I fill a measuring cup with fresh or frozen spinach. I then generally use half of a cucumber and a whole leaf of kale. *You can tear kale into small pieces and place in a measuring cup to approx. 1/4 cup.*

3) Place spinach in the food processor and blend until coarse. Add kale and cucumber and blend for 1 minute. Vegetables may still be mildly coarse — this is ok.

4) Add the meat, salt, and basil to the food processor. Blend until veggies and meat are thoroughly blended together.

5) Form meatballs or patties and place them in a glass Pyrex pan.

6) Cook at 300 degrees for 35 minutes or until thoroughly cooked.

Once meatballs or patties have cooled, freeze any leftovers and use at your convenience. It is essential to use unbleached parchment paper when freezing. Meatballs and patties will stick to the glass container and each other if they are not properly separated. To freeze line a square Pyrex container with parchment paper and layer according.

To reheat, simply place patties or meatballs in a Pyrex pan and cook for 10 minutes at 300 degrees (*or until warm*). The end result is a balanced dinner, lunch, or snack!

Please use this recipe as a base. We have found that this recipe is a great way to add vegetables to everyone's diet. In our family we initially started out with the base recipe and have gradually increased our veggie-to-meat ratio. We now use double or triple the amount of vegetables. For us it is truly a veggie burger! Modify this recipe to suit your taste buds and nutritional needs.

Chicken Nuggets

This was one of my son's favorite foods before he began the gluten-free/casein-free diet...and still is!

Health Benefits
Chicken is a very good source of protein, niacin, selenium, and vitamin B6. It is also a good source of pantothenic acid and phosphorous. The addition of almonds contributes additional protein, fiber, potassium, phosphorus, magnesium, calcium, iron, zinc, folic acid, and vitamins B2, B3, and E to this dish.

What you will need:

2 boneless, skinless organic free-range chicken breasts — free of antibiotics, hormones, and additives.

2 Tb. of melted ghee

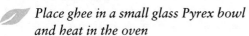 *Place ghee in a small glass Pyrex bowl and heat in the oven*

1 cup of pre-made frozen almond cookies

1/4 tsp. of Celtic sea salt

Large Glass Pyrex pan (9 x 13 in.)

Cuisinart Mini-Prep food processor or hand-held blender.

Steps:

1) Preheat oven to 250 degrees.

2) Combine frozen cookies and salt in handheld blender or mini food processor. Grind until you have the consistency of bread crumbs. *Make sure blender bowl is not wet — cookies will turn into a paste.*

3) Heat ghee in the oven to soften. Use a portion of the ghee to grease Pyrex pan. The rest is used to coat the chicken. You don't need to use a lot — just enough to make the cookie crumbs stick.

4) Wash chicken and cut into chunks or strips.

5) Rub ghee on chicken.

6) Sprinkle white cookie crumbs on both sides of the chicken and place in Pyrex pan.

7) Cook at 250 degrees for 45 minutes.

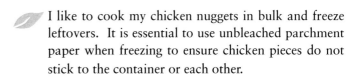 I like to cook my chicken nuggets in bulk and freeze leftovers. It is essential to use unbleached parchment paper when freezing to ensure chicken pieces do not stick to the container or each other.

To reheat, simply place frozen chicken pieces in Pyrex pan and cook at 250 degrees for 15 minutes or until warm.

I encourage everyone to use this recipe as a base and modify ingredients based on individual taste buds (more or less salt, agave, ghee, etc.).

Steak Bombs

These taste like they are right off your favorite pizzeria grill!

Health Benefits

Beef is an excellent source of protein and vitamins B12 and B6. It contains riboflavin, zinc, selenium, niacin, iron, and phosphorous. The addition of onions and peppers in this recipe contributes added vitamins and minerals such as calcium, magnesium, phosphorus, potassium, beta-carotene, folic acid, and vitamins C and B.

What you will need for steak bombs:

1lb. of organic, free-range grass fed top loin sirloin steak — free of antibiotics, hormones, and additives

1 organic onion

1 organic green pepper

1 tsp. of Celtic sea salt

1/2 Tb. of organic ghee

1/2 cup of Pacific Natural Foods brand organic vegetable broth.

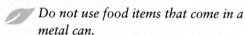 *Do not use food items that come in a metal can.*

Optional - 1/8 tsp. of organic ground pepper

Large Glass Pyrex pan (9 x 13 in.)

What you will need for wraps:

Organic Boston lettuce leaves or romaine lettuce, thoroughly washed

Or

any pre-made Mother Necessity rollups or flat breads (*see breads*)

What you will need for topping:

1 cup of diced organic tomato

1/4 cup of diced organic red onion

Optional - 2 Tb. of diced jalapeño (if you really want to spice things up!)

Steps for steak bombs:

1) Preheat oven to 300 degrees.

2) Combine vegetable broth and ghee in Pyrex pan.

3) Place pan in the oven until ghee is melted.

4) Cut sirloin, onion, and pepper into small, thin slices.

5) Remove Pyrex pan with melted ghee and vegetable broth from oven.

6) Combine all ingredients in pan: sirloin, onion, peppers, salt, and optional pepper.

7) Stir contents to evenly distribute all ingredients.

8) Cook at 300 degrees for 40 minutes or until steak is thoroughly cooked.

Steps for wraps and topping:

1) Combine diced tomato and onion topping in a bowl and mix.

2) Place thoroughly washed lettuce leaves on plate *or* any Mother Necessity breads or rollups.

3) Spoon steak bomb mixture on top of lettuce or MN breads and top with tomato and onion mixture and enjoy!

I encourage everyone to use this recipe as a base and modify ingredients based on individual taste buds (more or less broth, onions, peppers, ghee, etc.).

Side Dishes

All of Mother Necessity side dishes are easy to make and are packed with vitamins, minerals, amino acids and essentials fatty acids. Best yet, they taste like your favorite side dishes—without all of the potentially harmful additives or common allergens.

Mother Necessity's side dishes are compatible with any Mother Necessity Entrée. I advise everyone to mix and match, as the side dishes in this section are truly delicious!

I also encourage everyone to fill their plates with lightly cooked or steamed vegetables such as broccoli, asparagus, spinach, collard greens, kale, and other green leafy vegetables.

Vegetables are a rich source of vitamins, minerals, carbohydrates and protein. The little fat that vegetables contain is in the form of essential fatty acids. The more greens and vegetables we are able to implement into our diet, the more beneficial nutrients we will have to support proper health and renewal.

Stuffing

Stuffing is back and tastier than ever—you won't even be able to taste the difference between this recipe and the original.

Health Benefits

This savory dish not only tastes great but it is also packed with protein, fiber, potassium, magnesium, calcium, iron, zinc, folic acid, and vitamins B2, B3, and E. The organic vegetable broth used in this recipe contributes additional vitamins and minerals.

What you will need:

2 cups of pre-made frozen white cookies

1/2 cup of organic vegetable broth

 I recommend Pacific Natural Foods brand

2 Tb. of organic ghee

1/4 tsp. of Celtic sea salt or crystal Himalayan salt

Optional - 1/4 cup of organic diced celery

Optional - 1/4 cup of organic diced onion

Glass Pyrex glass pan (8 x 8 in.)

Steps:

1) Preheat oven to 250 degrees.

2) Place ghee in glass Pyrex pan and melt in the oven.

3) Take Pyrex pan with melted ghee out of the oven and combine (*whole*) cookies, salt, and vegetable broth in pan.

4) Stir contents and place pan in the oven.

5) Bake for 30 minutes at 250 degrees.

6) Stir contents with a fork or spoon every ten minutes, patting stuffing down (*to ensure stuffing is cooking evenly*)

7) After 30 minutes remove stuffing from the oven and give it a final stir. The end result is a delicious gluten-free/casein-free stuffing. Enjoy!

Stuffing can be baked longer to achieve desired texture. The longer you cook the crispier it will be.

Potatoes

Potatoes eaten in moderation can be a healthy treat!

Health Benefits
Potatoes are a very good source of vitamin C and a good source of vitamin B6, copper, potassium, manganese, and dietary fiber. The fiber content of a potato (with skin) equals that of many whole grain breads, pastas, and cereals. Potatoes also contain a variety of phytonutrients that have antioxidant activity. Among these important health-promoting compounds are carotenoids, flavonoids, and caffeic acid.

What you will need for Mashed Potatoes:

6 medium-sized organic potatoes.

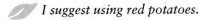 *I suggest using red potatoes.*

1/2 cup of Pacific Natural Foods brand vegetable broth

2 Tb. of organic ghee

1 tsp. of Celtic sea salt or crystal Himalayan salt

Optional - 1/4 tsp. of organic dulse granules with garlic – I use Maine Coast Sea Seasonings

What you will need for Homestyle potatoes:

6 medium-sized organic potatoes.

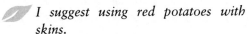 *I suggest using red potatoes with skins.*

1/2 cup of Pacific Natural Foods brand organic vegetable broth

1/2 cup of diced organic onions

1/2 cup of diced organic peppers

2 Tb. of organic ghee

1 tsp. of Celtic sea salt or crystal Himalayan salt

Large Pyrex pan (9 x 13 in.)

Steps for Mashed Potatoes:

1) Dice potatoes.

2) Place potatoes in boiling water and cook until tender.

3) Drain and rinse with purified water.

4) Combine potatoes with vegetable broth, ghee, salt and optional dulse seasoning.

5) Mix well with handheld mixer or potato masher.

This dish is wonderful with diced asparagus. I like to add my asparagus to the boiling water 5 minutes prior to draining and rinsing potatoes.

Steps for Homestyle Potatoes:

1) Preheat oven to 350 degrees.

2) Dice potatoes into cubes. *Skins can be left on or removed depending on your personal preference.*

3) Place ghee and vegetable broth into pan and place in the oven. Heat until ghee is melted.

4) Once ghee is melted, place remaining ingredients in pan: onions, peppers, salt, and potatoes.

5) Cook at 350 degrees for 40 minutes or until potatoes are at the desired firmness — stir frequently

This dish is very tasty with organic spinach. I like to add spinach to this dish in the last 15 minutes of cooking.

Sweet Potatoes

Sweet potatoes are rich in
vitamin C and flavor!

Health Benefits
Sweet potatoes are a very good source of dietary
fiber and potassium. They are also a good source
of beta carotene (a vitamin A equivalent nutrient),
vitamin C, and vitamins B1 and B6. In addition,
they contain potassium, iron, copper and manganese. Despite having the word "sweet" in their
name, sweet potatoes may be a beneficial food for
diabetics, as preliminary studies on animals have
revealed that they help to stabilize blood sugar levels
and lower insulin resistance.

What you will need for Mashed Sweet Potatoes:

3 organic medium-sized sweet potatoes
or yams

1/4 cup of organic vegetable broth
 *I like to use Pacific Natural Foods organic
vegetable broth.*

2 tsp. of vegetable glycerin

1 Tb. of organic unrefined coconut oil

1/2 tsp. of organic cinnamon

What you will need for Roasted Sweet Potatoes:

3 medium-sized sweet potatoes or yams

1/2 cup of organic vegetable broth
 *I like to use Pacific Natural Foods organic
vegetable broth.*

1/2 cup of diced organic onions

1/2 cup of diced organic peppers

1 Tb. of organic unrefined coconut oil

1/2 tsp. of Celtic sea salt or crystal
Himalayan salt

Large Glass Pyrex Pan (9 x 13 in.)

Steps for Mashed Sweet Potatoes:

1) Dice sweet potatoes.

2) Place sweet potatoes in boiling water and cook until
tender.

3) Drain and rinse with purified water.

4) Combine sweet potatoes with vegetable broth,
glycerin, coconut oil, and cinnamon.

5) Mix well with handheld mixer or potato masher
and they are ready to be served!

I like to steam kale leaves and spoon mashed sweet
potatoes into the middle. I then roll the leaf up and
have a delicious kale sweet potato roll up. Not only
does this make a wonderful looking side dish,
it also tastes amazing.

Steps for Roasted Sweet Potatoes:

1) Preheat oven to 350 degrees.

2) Dice sweet potatoes into cubes.

3) Place coconut oil and vegetable broth into glass
pan and place in the oven. Heat until coconut oil is
melted.

4) Place remaining ingredients into the pan: onions,
peppers, salt, and sweet potatoes.

5) Cook at 350 degrees for 40 minutes or until sweet
potatoes are at the desired firmness — stir frequently

This dish is very compatible with broccoli or any
vegetable for that matter. I like to add broccoli to
this dish in the last 15 minutes of cooking.

Rice – Quinoa, Millet and Brown

These rice dishes are fabulous when combined with lots of steamed veggies!

Health Benefits

The following gluten-free grains taste delicious! In addition they are high in protein, fiber, vitamins, and minerals. The grains I have chosen are easy to digest and are considered low-allergy grains.

What you will need for Quinoa:

1 cup of organic soaked quinoa

1/2 cup of purified water

1/2 cup of organic vegetable broth

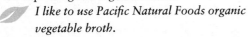 *I like to use Pacific Natural Foods organic vegetable broth.*

1 tsp. of organic ghee

1/2 tsp. of Celtic sea salt or crystal Himalayan salt

Optional – 1/2 tsp. of organic dulse with garlic - I use Maine Coast Sea Seasonings.

What you will need for Millet:

1 cup of organic soaked millet

1 ½ cups of purified water

1 cup of organic vegetable broth

1/2 tsp. of organic unrefined coconut oil

1 tsp. of Celtic sea salt or crystal Himalayan salt

Optional – 1/4 tsp. of organic kelp granules I use Maine Coast Sea Seasonings.

Optional – pinch of organic black pepper.

What you will need for Brown Rice:

1 cup of organic soaked brown rice

1 cup of purified water.

1 cup of organic vegetable broth

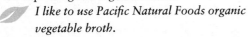 *I like to use Pacific Natural Foods organic vegetable broth.*

1/2 tsp. of organic unrefined coconut oil

3/4 tsp. of Celtic sea salt or crystal Himalayan salt

Optional – 1/2 tsp. of organic dulse with garlic – I use Maine Coast Sea Seasonings.

Steps for Quinoa:

1) Soak quinoa for 8 hours.

2) Rinse well in purified water.

3) Place broth and water in a glass stovetop friendly pan and bring to a boil.

4) Combine quinoa, ghee, and salt.

5) Reduce heat and simmer, stirring frequently.

6) Cook for 20 to 25 minutes or until desired consistency is reached.

 This dish tastes wonderful with the addition of diced organic celery, carrots and onion. I add these ingredients to the pot when adding quinoa, ghee and salt.

Steps for Millet:

1) Soak millet for 8 hours.

2) Rinse well in purified water.

3) Place broth and water in a glass stovetop friendly pan and bring to a boil.

4) Combine millet, coconut oil, and salt.

5) Reduce heat and simmer, stirring frequently.

6) Cook for 20 to 25 minutes or until desired consistency is reached.

7) When rice is cooked remove from burner and add optional kelp granules and black pepper.

 If you really want to spice this rice up add ¼ cup of organic tomatoes, 2 tb. of organic jalapenos, and a pinch of organic cayenne pepper.

Steps for Brown Rice:

1) Soak brown rice for 8 hours.

2) Rinse well in purified water.

3) Place broth and water in a glass stovetop friendly pan and bring to a boil.

4) Combine brown rice, coconut oil, and salt.

5) Reduce heat and simmer, stirring frequently.

6) Cook for 35 to 40 minutes or until desired consistency is reached.

7) When rice is cooked remove from burner and add optional dulse with garlic.

 This recipe tastes delicious with ¼ cup of organic diced onions, peppers and broccoli. I add these ingredients to the pot when adding brown rice, coconut oil and salt.

Roasted Squash and Zucchini

This dish is packed full of taste and nutrition.

Health Benefits
These roasted vegetables are packed with nutrients such as carotenes, potassium, calcium, magnesium, folic acid, and vitamins B and C. This dish is a wonderful source of fiber, antioxidants, and even has some antiviral properties.

What you will need:

1 organic summer squash

1 organic zucchini

1 cup of sliced or diced organic onion

1 cup of fresh or frozen organic broccoli

1 cup of Pacific Natural Food brand organic vegetable broth

1 tsp. of Celtic sea salt or crystal Himalayan salt

Large Glass Pyrex pan (9 x 13 in.)

Steps:

1) Preheat oven to 250 degrees.

2) Thoroughly wash all vegetables.

3) Dice or slice squash, zucchini, and onion.

4) Pour vegetable broth into Pyrex pan.

5) Add squash, zucchini, onion, broccoli, and salt.

6) Stir all ingredients to thoroughly combine broth and vegetables.

7) Cook vegetables for 35 to 40 minutes stirring frequency

8) Remove from oven after 35 to 40 minutes depending on desired consistency.

In addition to the vegetables mentioned, I also like to add kale or collard greens to this dish, which contributes additional nutrients and a fabulous taste!

Garden Salad with Italian Dressing

A salad is the perfect accompaniment to any entrée. I encourage everyone to try as many different greens and vegetables as possible, to broaden their nutritional intake.

Health Benfits:
The following salad is a very basic, quick salad that I like to whip up. I have developed a very alkaline, cleansing, Italian dressing that compliments the vitamin and mineral content of this salad.

What you will need:

1 head of organic romaine lettuce

1 organic turnip

1 organic tomato

1 organic cucumber

1/2 cup of organic broccoli sprouts

Optional — 1/4 cup of organic red onion

What you will need for salad dressing:

1/2 cup of organic unrefined apple cider vinegar

2 Tb. of vegetable glycerin.

I like to use Frontier brand.

1 Tb. of purified water

1/8 tsp. of basil

1/8 tsp. of thyme

1 Tb. of organic unrefined olive oil

Steps for salad:

1) Thoroughly wash all vegetables.

2) Chop romaine lettuce into small bite-size pieces.

3) Peel turnip and dice into small pieces.

4) Dice tomato, cumcumber and optional onion.

5) Toss all ingredients in a bowl with sprouts.

Steps for salad dressing:

1) Combine all ingredients in a handheld blender or whisk ingredients in a bowl.

2) Top salad with salad dressing and enjoy!

In addition to a side dish, salad makes a great entrée. We enjoy this salad topped with Mother Necessity rice, chicken fingers, or steak bombs. I encourage everyone to be as creative as possible!

Mother Necessity Pies

Pies can now be enjoyed by all who cannot tolerate gluten or casein. The following pie recipes are rich in amino acids, vitamins, minerals, and essential fatty acids. Best yet, they are completely free of gluten, casein, corn, and soy and do not contain any refined flours or sugar.

Mother Necessity Apple Pie is packed with beneficial nutrients. The Millet pie crust used in this recipe is high in protein and rich in magnesium, potassium, phosphorus, and B vitamins. The apples in this recipe are a good source of calcium, magnesium, phosphorus, vitamin C, and beta-carotene.

Mother Necessity Blueberry Pie contains vitamins B1, B2, B3, and B6 as well as manganese, iron, selenium, magnesium, phosphorous, and trace minerals. Brown rice is a wonderful source of protein and amino acids, and is recommended as a low-allergy alternative grain. The blueberries used in this recipe are an excellent source of flavonoids, vitamin C, soluble fiber, and insoluble fibers such as pectin.

Mother Necessity Pumpkin Pie *with crust,* is high in protein and rich in magnesium, potassium, phosphorus, and B vitamins. This wonderful pie looks and tastes like "traditional" pumpkin pie, yet it is packed with plenty of protein, fiber, and B vitamins. The carrots in this pie are an excellent antioxidant source and contain beta-carotene and an abundance of vitamins and minerals. The pumpkin seeds in this pie contribute valuable omega-3 fatty acids, and supplies minerals such as magnesium, calcium, iron, manganese, and zinc.

All Mother Necessity pies are equally healthy and nutritious. I encourage everyone to try all Mother Necessity pies as there is a pie for every occasion!

Apple Pie

This delicious pie is just as good as the original—with a healthy twist.

What you will need for pie crust:

2/3 cup of organic soaked millet

2/3 cup of purified water

1/2 Tb. of organic coconut oil

1/2 tsp. of Celtic sea salt or crystal Himalayan salt.

Round Glass Pyrex Pan

Cuisinart Mini-Prep food processor or Vitamix

What you will need for apple filling:

2 cups of organic apples

2 Tb. of organic raw agave

2 Tb. of purified water

1 tsp. of organic cinnamon

1/2 tsp. of organic cloves

1 Tb. of organic coconut oil (*melted*)

1 tsp. of organic fresh lemon juice

Large bowl food processor

What you will need for apple pie topping:

3 pre-made almond muffins (*See Muffins and Cupcakes section*).

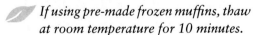 *If using pre-made frozen muffins, thaw at room temperature for 10 minutes.*

If you do not have any almond muffins pre-made, you can substitute 1 cup of pre-made almond cookies out of the freezer. Coarsely grind in a mini-prep food processor or handheld blender.

Steps for crust:

1) Soak millet in a jar for a minimum of 8 hrs. or overnight. Rinse well (*3 to 4 times*) and drain.

2) Preheat oven to 350 degrees.

3) Grease pyrex glass pan with 1/2 Tb. of melted organic coconut oil. Spread evenly.

4) After soaking and rinsing grain, place grain in Cuisinart mini food processor and grind for 1 minute or until fully ground.

5) Add remaining ingredients: water and salt. Grind for an additional 1 to 2 minutes. *If using a Vitamix, all ingredients can be combined and blended at the same time.*

6) Pour batter into glass Pyrex pan with coconut oil. *Always grind batter right before pouring into pan. Grain has a tendency to settle on the bottom when left to sit.*

7) Stir combined ingredients in the pan with a slow whisking motion to ensure that coconut oil, water, and grain are evenly distributed.

8) Bake crust at 350 degrees for 35 minutes.

9) While crust is baking prepare apple filling.

Steps for apple filling:

1) Wash apples with purified water. Peel and chop apples.

2) Combine apples and apple filling ingredients in food processor: agave, water, cloves, cinnamon, melted coconut oil and lemon juice

3) Blend until coarsely chopped.

4) Remove pie crust from oven after baking for 25 minutes

5) Reduce heat to 250 degrees

6) Add apple filling to crust

7) Cook pie for an additional 20 minutes at a reduced temperature of 250 degrees.

8) Prepare apple pie topping

Steps for apple topping:

1) After baking pie for a total of 45 minutes, remove pie from oven. Crumble almond muffins and sprinkle them on top of pie (*1 cup of ground almond cookies can be substituted if almond muffins are not available*).

Blueberry Pie

This is a delicious addition to any holiday!

Health Benefits
The blueberries used in this pie are an excellent source of flavonoids, vitamin C, soluble fiber, and insoluble fibers such as pectin. In addition, blueberries contain manganese, vitamin E, and riboflavin.

What you will need for pie crust:

3/4 cup of organic soaked brown rice

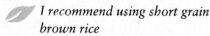 *I recommend using short grain brown rice*

2/3 cup of purified water

1 tsp. of organic unrefined coconut oil

1/2 tsp. of Celtic sea salt or crystal Himalayan salt

Round glass Pyrex pan

Cuisinart Mini-Prep food processor or Vitamix

What you will need for blueberry filling:

2 cups of fresh organic blueberries

 *frozen blueberries will be too runny*

3 Tb. of organic raw agave

1/2 Tb. of organic vanilla flavoring

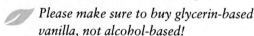 *Please make sure to buy glycerin-based vanilla, not alcohol-based!*

1 tsp. of fresh organic lemon juice

Mini Prep food processor or handheld blender

Steps for crust:

1) Soak brown rice in a jar for a minimum of 8 hours or overnight. Rinse well (3 to 4 times) and drain.

2) Preheat oven to 350 degrees.

3) Grease pyrex glass pan with 1 tsp. of melted organic coconut oil. Spread evenly.

4) After soaking and rinsing grain, place grain in Cuisinart mini food processor and grind for 1 minute or until fully ground.

5) Add remaining ingredients: water and salt. Grind for an additional 1 to 2 minutes. *If using a Vitamix, all ingredients can be combined and blended at the same time.*

6) Pour batter into glass Pyrex pan with coconut oil. *Always grind batter right before pouring into pan. Grain has a tendency to settle on the bottom when left to sit—especially brown rice!*

7) Stir combined ingredients in the pan with a slow whisking motion to ensure that coconut oil, water, and grain are evenly distributed.

8) Bake crust at 350 degrees for 35 minutes.

9) While crust is baking prepare blueberry filling.

Steps for blueberry filling:

1) Wash blueberries with purified water.

2) Place all ingredients in a food processor or handheld blender: blueberries, agave, water, vanilla, and fresh lemon juice.

3) Blend until coarsely chopped (*we do not want to purée pie filling*) only process filling for 15-30 seconds.

4) Remove pie crust from oven after baking for 35 minutes

5) Reduce oven heat to 250 degrees

6) Add blueberry filling to crust

7) Cook pie for an additional 20 minutes at a reduced temperature of 250 degrees

8) Let pie sit until cool. Cut and serve!

Traditional Pumpkin Pie with Crust

This pie is perfect for any occasion.

What you will need for pie crust:

2/3 cup of organic soaked millet

2/3 cup of purified water

1/2 Tb. of organic unrefined coconut oil

1/2 tsp. of Celtic sea salt or crystal Himalayan salt

Round Glass Pyrex Pan

Cuisinart Mini-Prep food processor or Vitamix

What you will need pie filling:

1 cup of soaked organic pumpkin seeds

1 ½ organic carrots (or 1 cup)

4 Tb. of organic raw agave

1 Tb. of Frontier organic vanilla flavoring

 Please make sure to buy glycerin-based vanilla, not alcohol-based!

1 tsp. of organic cinnamon

1/4 tsp. of organic ground cloves

1/4 cup of purified water

Large-bowl food processor

Steps for crust:

1) Soak millet in a jar for a minimum of 8 hours or overnight. Rinse well and drain.

2) Preheat oven to 350 degrees.

3) Grease pyrex glass pan with 1/2 Tb. of melted organic coconut oil. Spread evenly.

4) After soaking and rinsing grain, place grain in Cuisinart mini food processor and grind for 1 minute or until fully ground.

5) Add remaining ingredients: water and salt. Grind for an additional 1 to 2 minutes. *If using a Vitamix, all ingredients can be combined and blended at the same time.*

6) Pour batter into glass Pyrex pan with coconut oil. *Always grind batter right before pouring into pan.*

7) Stir combined ingredients in the pan with a slow whisking motion to ensure that coconut oil, water, and grain are evenly distributed.

8) Bake crust at 350 degrees for 35 minutes.

9) While crust is baking prepare pumpkin filling.

Steps for pie filling:

1) Soak pumpkin seeds for a minimum of 8 hours or overnight. Rinse well (*3 to 4 times*) and drain.

2) Place carrots in food processor and blend until coarse.

3) Combine remaining ingredients: pumpkin seeds, water, agave, vanilla, cinnamon, and cloves.

4) Blend for 2 to 3 minutes. Pause two or three times using a spoon to scrape any loose ingredients from the sides of the bowl and under the blade. Blend until you have a relatively smooth batter.

5) Remove pie crust from the oven after baking for 20 minutes.

6) Reduce oven heat to 250 degrees.

7) Add pumpkin filling to crust.

8) Cook pie for an additional 25 minutes at a reduced temperature of 250 degrees.

9) When pie is done, remove from oven and let cool before serving.

"Crustless" Pumpkin Pie

This pie is big on taste and nutrition!

Health Benefits
This pie contains valuable omega-3 fatty acids, and minerals such as magnesium, calcium, iron, manganese, and zinc. Mother Necessity's pumpkin pie is packed with plenty of protein, fiber and B vitamins. The carrots in this pie are an excellent source of antioxidants, beta-carotene, and vitamin A.

What you will need:

1 cup of soaked organic pumpkin seeds

1 ½ organic carrots (or 1 cup)

4 Tb. of organic raw agave

1 Tb. of Frontier organic vanilla flavoring

 Please make sure to buy glycerin-based vanilla, not alcohol-based!

1 tsp. of organic cinnamon

1/4 tsp. of organic ground cloves

1/2 cup of purified water

1 tsp. of organic unrefined coconut oil

Round glass Pyrex pan

Large-bowl food processor

Steps:

1) Soak pumpkin seeds for a minimum of 8 hours or overnight. Rinse well (*3 to 4 times*) and drain.

2) Preheat oven to 285 degrees.

3) Place coconut oil in glass Pyrex pan and melt.

4) Place carrots in food processor and blend until coarse.

5) Combine remaining ingredients: pumpkin seeds, water, agave, vanilla, cinnamon, and cloves.

6) Blend for 2 to 3 minutes. Pause two or three times using a spoon to scrape any loose ingredients from the sides of the bowl and under the blade. Blend until you have a relatively smooth batter.

7) Take the Pyrex pan with melted coconut oil out of oven and place pumpkin pie mix into pan.

8) Cook pie at 285 degrees for 45 minutes.

9) When pie is done, remove from oven and let cool before serving.

This pie is wonderful served chilled or warmed.
I encourage everyone to use this recipe as a base and modify ingredients based on individual taste buds (more or less agave, carrots cinnamon, etc.).

Apple Crisp

Quick, easy, delicious, and healthy!

Health Benefits
Apples are a good source of calcium, magnesium, phosphorus, vitamin C, and beta-carotene. They also contain fiber and pectin, both of which promote bowel regularity and help escort toxins out of the body. The addition of almonds in this recipe contributes protein, fiber, potassium, magnesium, calcium, iron, zinc, folic acid, and vitamins B2, B3, and E.

What you will need for apple crisp:

2 cups of organic apples

(washed, peeled, and cubed)

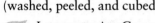 *I suggest using Granny Smith apples.*

2 Tb. of organic raw agave

2 Tb. of purified water

1 tsp. of organic cinnamon

1/2 tsp. of organic cloves

1 Tb. of organic unrefined coconut oil

1 tsp. of organic fresh lemon juice

Round or square Pyrex pan

What you will need for apple crisp topping:

4 pre-made almond muffins (*See Muffins and Cupcakes section*).

 If using pre-made frozen muffins, thaw at room temperature for 10 minutes.

If you do not have any almond muffins pre-made you can substitute 1 cup of pre-made almond cookies out of the freezer. Coarsely grind in a mini-prep food processor or handheld blender.

Steps for apple crisp:

1) Preheat oven to 250 degrees.

2) Place coconut oil in round Pyrex Pan and place in oven to melt.

3) Wash apples with purified water. Peel and coarsely chop apples.

4) Place apples in a bowl and combine remaining ingredients: agave, water, cinnamon, lemon juice and cloves.

5) Stir with a spoon—do not use food processor.

6) Take Pyrex pan out of the oven when coconut oil is melted.

7) Add apple filling to Pyrex pan and cook for 20 minutes.

Steps for apple crisp topping:

1) After cooking apple filling for 20 minutes remove apple mixture from the oven.

2) Stir ingredients.

3) Crumble pre-made almond muffins and sprinkle them on top of apples. Pat down with a spoon. *Coarsely chopped almond cookies can be used as a substitute.*

4) Place apple mixture back in the oven and cook for an additional 10 minutes.

5) When ready. Take apple crisp out of the oven and let cool.

6) Serve and enjoy!

I encourage everyone to use this recipe as a base and modify ingredients based on individual taste buds (more or less agave, apples cinnamon, etc.).

Chocolate Mousse Pie

This pie is heavenly!

Health Benefits

Mother Necessity's chocolate mousse pie contains protein, fiber, potassium, magnesium, calcium, iron, zinc, folic acid, and vitamins B2, B3, and E. Almonds have been found to play an effective role in lowering cholesterol and reducing heart disease. The chocolate in this pie contributes a significant amount of magnesium and is a rich source of flavonoids and antioxidants.

What you will need for mousse filling:

1/2 cup of soaked organic almonds

1/8 cup of purified water

2 Tb. of organic raw agave

3 Tb. of organic vanilla flavoring

 Please make sure to buy glycerin-based vanilla, not alcohol-based!

1/2 tsp. of melted organic unrefined coconut oil

2 Tb. of organic unsweetened chocolate powder

 I suggest using raw organic chocolate powder

Large Food Processor

What you will need for crust:

Round glass Pyrex pan

2 cups of pre-made organic almond cookies (*room temperature*) See "Cookie" section.

2 Tb. of purified water

Large Food Processor

Steps for crust:

1) Place room temperature almond cookies in food processor with 2 Tb. of purified water.

2) Process for approx. 1 to 2 minutes (*mixture will be coarsely chopped*). Pause occasionally to scrape any loose ingredients from the sides of food processor.

3) Remove cookie mixture from food processor and spoon into round Pyrex pan.

4) Press down firmly to pack down mixture evenly, like a crust.

Steps for mousse:

1) Combine all of the mousse filling ingredients into the food processor: almonds, agave, vanilla, coconut oil, chocolate and water.

2) Blend for 2 to 3 minutes or until smooth. Pause 3 to 4 times and take a spoon to scrape any loose ingredients from the sides of the bowl and below the blade. Blend until you have a relatively smooth mixture.

3) Pour batter into pie crust.

4) Freeze pie for a minimum of 3 hours before serving.

5) Take out of freezer and enjoy!

I encourage everyone to use this recipe as a base and modify ingredients based on individual taste buds (more or less coconut oil, agave, chocolate, etc.).

Sproutpeople offer organic sprouting seeds and equipment. www.sproutpeople.com

Big Tree Organic Farm offers quality, organic almonds. www.bigtreeorganic.com

Jaffe Brothers offers organic nuts, seeds, grains, raw carob, sprouting equipment and organic foods. www.organicfruitsandnuts.com

Handy Pantry offers organic spouting seeds and equipment. www.handypantry.com

Excalibur offers high quality dehydrating machines. www.excaliburdehydrator.com

Kerr and Ball glass canning jars can be found at www.freshpreserving.com

Foodsaver offers vacuums to seal glass canning jars (need to purchase vacuum and widemouth sealing accessory). www.foodsaver.com

Madhava offers quality organic raw agave. www.madhavahoney.com

Frontier Coop offers vegetable glycerin, organic spices, alcohol-free flavorings, and much, much, more visit www.frontiercoop.com

Natures First law offers organic raw chocolate powder, and other organic foods. www.superfoods.com

Purity Farms produces high quality organic Ghee (clarified butter) that is lactose free and casein free. www.purityfarms.com

Pacific Natural Foods offers organic vegetable broth and other organic foods. www.pacificfoods.com

Beyond Gourmet offers unbleached baking cups and parchment paper. These items can be found at most health foods stores and various online stores.

Arrowhead Mills offers organic whole grains such as quinoa and millet. They can be found at most health food stores and online. www.arrowheadmills.com

Braun Handheld Multiquick Blender with Chopper can be found at Target, Linen N' Things, Bed & Bath and other various home good stores and webstores. www.braun.com

Cuisinart Mini-Prep Plus Food Processor can be found at Target, Linen N' Things, Bed & Bath and other various home good stores and webstores. www.cuisinart.com

Kitchenaid Large Food Processor can be found at Linen N' Things, Bed & Bath and other various home good stores and webstores. www.kitchenaid.com

Vita-Mix is a powerful juicer, grinder and blender that can be found online at www.vitamix.com

Bionaturae offers organic tomato paste in a glass jar. www.bionaturae.com

The Grain & Salt Society offers Celtic Sea Salt authentic, unprocessed whole salt from the coastal regions of France. www.celticseasalt.com

Lundberg Family Farms offers organic short grain rice. They can be found in most healthfood stores and online. www.lundberg.com

Mother Necessity offers all natural, whole food supplements (greens, probiotic/enzymes, liver support, detox solutions), GF/CF books, recipes, healthy living consultations and GF/CF whole food cooking classes. www.mothernecessity.com

notes

Dylan's Story

Overcoming Autism, A Childhood Epidemic.

Cristin Fergus
President

Joseph Fergus
Vice President

Dylan's Story is the account of one family's journey to recover their son from Autism through extensive research, nutrition, and the elimination of chemicals.

Dylan's Story details contributing factors which were the underlying cause of Dylan's Autism. The book contains extensive research on sources of common food allergens, chemicals and toxins and their effect on the digestive system, central nervous system, brain, and immune system. The indepth Resource Guide lists common chemicals and toxins, food additives, GMO's, preservatives, heavy metals, vaccinations, refined foods, GF/CF diet and much, much more. The book is the result of the research that enabled two parents to acquire the knowledge necessary to make changes in their son's diet and environment to overcome his Autism.

Dylan's Story includes recipes that Cristin Fergus, CNC, has developed for Dylan. They are organic "whole" food recipes that are corn free, gluten free, casein free, and soy free. The recipes have been developed based on their nutritional profiles. They are healthy alternatives which helped Dylan eliminate toxins and common allergens from his diet, while supporting better health!

Information in this book can benefit anyone who suffers from allergies, chronic health problems or neurological dysfunction.

MOTHER Necessity
Supplements, Books and Organic Foods

"After extensively researching nutritional products, Joe and I developed the **Mother Necessity** supplement line out of "necessity." As we became aware of the challenges of trying to find pure, whole food products, we wanted to offer high quality whole food nutrition – free of fillers, additives, isolated nutrients and synthetic ingredients … *Nutrition that people can trust!*

In and effort to recover our son's health, we have come to understand that the body can never obtain optimal health until it is provided with the nutrients to support proper brain function, body function, and detoxification. We believe there are many natural interventions that can encourage healing, but our personal view is that proper nutrition and chemical avoidance are the foundation which make all other interventions that much more effective.

Mother Necessity is committed to offering the highest quality nutritional products to naturally strengthen the body and support good health. Joe and I are passionate in ensuring that Mother Necessity offers only all natural products that we personally believe in, and use in our own family."

Cristin Fergus

MOTHER Necessity

PO Box 1496, Bonita Springs, FL 34133
email: information@mothernecessity.com
Toll Free 877 -266-1022
www.mothernecessity.com

To learn more about MN books, products and services visit www.mothernecessity.com or call 877-266-1022.

MOTHER Necessity

All-Natural Supplements

Helping to Grow a Healthy Generation!

The Mother Necessity Pledge

Mother Necessity is committed to offering the highest quality nutritional products with the highest intention. We at Mother Necessity pledge to use only the finest ingredients that Mother Nature has to offer.

MOTHER Necessity *New!*

2 in 1 PROBIOTIC ENZYMES

Supports Digestion and Intestinal Health!

Mother Necessity 2 in 1 Probiotic Enzymes are a comprehensive formula that works synergistically to support proper digestion and intestinal health. Our probiotic enzymes are a combination of beneficial soil based probiotics and plant enzymes, both of which are essential to the digestion process and the production of many vitamins and minerals. When taken together probiotics and plant enzymes work simultaneously to increase the absorption, assimilation and utilization of nutrients, while lessening the demands on the body. Enzymes and probiotics break down proteins for easy assimilation and assure greater levels of digestion. They also have the ability to neutralize toxins, inhibit yeast/unfriendly bacterial growth, and support overall immune function.

MOTHER Necessity

DETOX SOLUTIONS

Removing Toxins Mother Nature's Way

Mother Necessity Detox Solution contains a special blend of all natural cleansing and detoxifying ingredients. Use Mother Necessity Detox Solution to gently remove toxins and chemicals naturally and effectively while supporting intestinal health. *Can be used both internally and externally.*

MOTHER Necessity

ESSENTIAL GREENS

Mother Natures Vitamins and Minerals

Mother Necessity Essential Greens are beneficial for cleansing, detoxifying, and supporting nutritional needs. Essential Greens have been carefully formulated to support liver, kidney, blood, circulation and immune function. Mother Necessity Essential Greens are Organic/Wildcrafted and contain a synergistic blend of all natural vitamins, minerals, antioxidants, essential fatty acids, probiotics, phytonutrients, soluble and insoluble fiber, chlorophyll, amino acids and enzymes. Mother Necessity Essential Greens are balanced by nature, and contain whole food nutrients that are easily utilized and assimilated by the body.

MOTHER Necessity *New!*

SEA OF GREENS DETOX BATH

A Revitalizing Nutritional Cleanse for the Whole Body!

Mother Necessity Sea of Greens naturally cleanses and detoxifies the body while replenishing vital nutrients to support optimal health. Mother Necessity Sea of Greens is a synergistic blend of some of the most detoxifying, fortifying, and revitalizing nutrients that Mother Nature has to offer. Use this mineral rich, alkalizing bath to naturally and effectively detox and remineralize the whole body. *Can be used both internally and externally.*

MOTHER Necessity *Now with Organic Goji!*

LIVER SUPPORT

Supporting proper liver function for optimal health!

Proper liver function is essential for good health. Mother Necessity Liver Support is designed to help strengthen and detoxify the liver to promote healthy liver function and the elimination of toxins. Mother Necessity Liver Support provides natural protection against toxic burdens and environmental stress.

MOTHER Necessity *Coming Soon!*

ESSENTIAL FRUITS

Whole food vitamin C and antioxidants

Mother Necessity Essential Fruits is comprised of all-natural, organic/wild crafted "super" fruits that provide whole food vitamin C. Mother Necessity Essential Fruits deliver health boosting phytonutrients, enzymes, probiotics, vitamins, minerals, and potent antioxidants to support proper immune function and combat free radical damage.

MOTHER *Necessity* ™

Gluten-Free/Casein Free Ice Cream, Smoothies & Protein Shake Recipes

By Cristin Fergus

MOTHER *Necessity*

Finally... Healthy Ice Cream, Smoothies & Protein Shakes for Everyone

Whole Food, Organic, Gluten Free/Casein Free Recipe
Free of Common Allergens!

- Soy Free
- Dairy Free
- Gluten Free
- No Refined Sugar

HIGH-PROTEIN
ICE CREAM
SMOOTHIES
& SHAKES